Treatment of

EXOTIC
MARINE FISH
DISEASES

Pet Reference Series No. 1

Edward Kingsford, M.D.

**The
Palmetto
Publishing
Company**

4747 - 28th Street North • St. Petersburg, Florida
(813) 522-3453
33714

Library of Congress Cataloging in Publication Data

Kingsford, Edward, 1928-
    Treatment of exotic marine fish diseases.

    (Pet reference series; no. 1)
    1.   Marine aquarium fishes--Diseases. I. Title.
[DNLM: 1.   Fish diseases--Therapy. SH171 K55t]
SF458.5.K5   639'.34   75-26516
ISBN 0-915096-03-X

This book has been set in Optima Medium 10 point by Photocomp using a
computerized process and printed in America by the Great Outdoors Press, St.
Petersburg, Florida.

ACKNOWLEDGEMENT

This manual is dedicated to my wife, Frances, who has given much of her time and devotion to this effort; and to Michael Weinberg whose enthusiasm and help as well as donation of many important specimens have made this effort possible. Special credit should be given to those who supported the technical aspects of the investigations for this book, Daniel M. Lev, M.D., Henry Loun, Joan Rotz and Marilyn Massey.

CONTENTS

The 1950's and 60's were the decades of space exploration. Man's science and industry were turned outward toward the mysteries of the moon, the solar system and outer space. Now, however, our interests are returning to the problems and beauties of our home planet, and the challenges of the least known three-fourths of the globe, the earth's oceans. Perhaps the 1970's and 80's will be the decades of exploration and propagation of the resources of the sea.

Although only a favored few could personally experience the glory of space flight, all who wish to can explore the undersea world by keeping and studying a marine aquarium. Some of us can also apply our "earthly" skills to this "new" environment and make significant contributions to our knowledge of the sea and her inhabitants with our spare time hobby. Dr. Ed Kingsford has done just this through the original research and effort he has put into this manual on marine fish disease.

Dr. Kingsford, a practicing pathologist and M.D., has turned his considerable talents to a field where there is much misinformation and confusion. Marine fish pathology has long been primarily a descriptive discipline since developed nations did not propagate marine or brackish fish and the literature concentrates on identification and description of naturally occurring diseases. The question has always been "What killed the fish?"; rather than "How can they be cured?" Most treatments for marine fish are borrowed from fresh water culturists and very often disease is diagnosed from fresh water literature.

Dr. Kingsford began at the very beginning by performing extensive pathological research to determine the real cause of typical marine tropical fish disease symptoms. Once the causitive organisms and the symptoms were firmly linked through microscopic and histological analysis, he then systematically determined the effectiveness of chemical and antibiotic treatments. Thus this book is not a compilation from extant literature on fish diseases, but a new contribution based on original research and extensive experimentation.

The marine aquarium enthusiast will find a fresh approach to disease diagnoses and treatment and can gain much new information in these pages. This manual will also find wide use by those engaged in the development of mariculture, breeding and maintaining marine food fish as well as tropical ornamental fish.

Martin A. Moe, Jr.
Marine Biologist

1. INTRODUCTION

This manual for the treatment of sick marine fish has been designed for the aquarist who has already mastered the techniques for maintaining water quality.Even so,the importance of water quality must be stressed as the first and paramount objective in keeping healthy marine fish. But perfect water quality alone will not maintain fish in a state of lasting good health. And herein lies the frustration and lament of the fish culturist, aquarist and hobbyist. When wild exotic marine fish are caught, they always seem healthy and vigorous. This is because in nature debilitated fish are quickly eaten. On the reef it is the survival of the fittest, and one slow response is usually the last. While one does not generally see sick fish when collecting, nevertheless they do carry diseases; a fact that has been amply demonstrated by subsequent autopsy. After hundreds of complete autopsies on coral reef fish from many oceans of the world and microscopic examination of all organs, the occurrence of several or more diseases in *all* wild fish has been well established.

Because the disease is often in the carrier state or quiescent, the fish appear healthy and are able to evade their natural enemies. Under adverse conditions, pathogenic (disease producing) organisms may multiply within the fish producing overt signs of disease. Such adverse conditions include the trauma of shipping, overcrowding, fin nipping, low oxygen tension, high ammonia or nitrite level, low pH, starvation or improper diet, bacterial blooms from overfeeding, and many others. Fish have several natural defense mechanisms enabling them to hold many diseases in balance or in a carrier state. But such defense mechanisms are easily overwhelmed in captivity with dissemination of certain diseases to every tank inhabitant. By maintaining high standards of water quality and nutrition we promote the natural defense mechanisms of the fish. Immunity is one mechanism demonstrated in fishes, and varies among genera in

1

its degree of development. It depends on antibodies, the defense proteins that are formed in response to infection by a specific organism; and for a fish to have such antibodies implies prior exposure to that disease. When fish from different areas are placed together they may succumb from an overwhelming exposure to a new disease for which they have no antibodies because they have not been previously exposed. Fish have other body defenses such as lysozymes and an antiviral substance, interferon. But while these mechanisms are of great importance in their natural habitat, they are totally inadequate under aquarium conditions in the closed system. Fish have five major disease categories that are protozoan, bacterial, or fungal in origin.

Two of the most important protozoan parasites of coral reef fish have life cycles that hold the parasites in balance in the sea but in the tank are too effective. These are *Oodinium* and *Cryptocaryon*. In both cases, a free swimming stage in the life cycle attacks the fish, matures, drops off, and produces a multitude of new infective free swimming offspring. In the oceans, the balance of nature prevails between fish and protozoan parasite because of a dilution factor and currents that may carry the infective organisms away. But in the tank, superinfection results in the death of most fish occupants. Unfortunately, these two diseases are found in all oceans where coral reef fish abound and wild or newly collected fish can be expected to carry them almost invariably, although some seasonal variation in incidence will be experienced.

Another disease that appears to be ubiquitous is tuberculosis. This is not the same as human tuberculosis, but caused by closely related species of *Mycobacteria*. The rate of infection is much less than with *Oodinium* and *Cryptocaryon*, but frequent enough to warrant routine cleansing treatment.

Another almost universal problem is trematode infestation of the gut which may extend to liver, obstruct the biliary tract, or cause perforation of gut wall and death.

The fifth major disease problem is bacterial infection. This may be devastating in the closed system aquarium.

Another disease that has been found in most fish autopsied from the warm oceans is *Ichthyophonus*, or a closely related internal fungus. In some fish, the organisms are walled off with the formation of granulomas. While in others the organism is disseminated in many organs and is frequently the cause of death.

The above named diseases cause at least 95% of deaths from disease among exotic marine fish in the salt water aquarium. Their control is the major objective of this manual, and the most important precept should be that EVERY WILD FISH REQUIRES CLEANSING TREATMENT regardless of how vigorous he appears or how clean the water in which he was captured. It is important to remember that treated fish will not remain "clean" if one untreated fish is added to the tank. It may be necessary then to re-treat all fish in the tank. Cleansing treatment of all fish is well worth the effort and survival will be measured in years instead of weeks. The important diseases mentioned cover the taxonomic field, i.e., bacteria, fungi, protozoa and metazoa, and it is impossible to expect one drug to cure them all in spite of some of the grandiose claims advertised.

When several medications are required, the system of treatment is equally important for fish survival. Some drugs interfere with others and cannot be used simultaneously. Drugs administered in strong enough dosage to be effective also stress the fish and may well result in their death if the disease is too advanced when treatment is started. This is frequently the case and it is much better to treat the fish immediately after they are collected while they are still vigorous than to wait until they show definite signs of disease and debilitation. Furthermore, fish frequently stop eating early in the course of a disease which may make treatment impossible.

Most of the fish collected for the salt water aquarium are juveniles and may not live for more than five to seven days without food. Some will not eat for the first few days in captivity, and others will not eat with certain medications in the water. So the first week in captivity is crucial to the long survival of fish in marine aquaria, and treatment should begin as soon as they are collected.

In addition to the cleansing treatment of all wild fish, there will be occasions when fish that have appeared well in established tanks break out with disease and will require treatment. It will be found impractical and unnecessary to treat such fish for all the common diseases. Accurate diagnosis is necessary, followed by vigorous treatment for the one disease. A wrong diagnosis usually results in dead fish. Early recognition that the fish is sick and prompt treatment is the key to success. This urgency is exemplified by *Oodinium ocellatum* infection where fish may be noted breathing fast one evening and the next morning half of them are found lying on the bottom panting; by afternoon they are dead. While the infection does not always proceed this fast, it may do so under crowded conditions. Bacterial infections may have a similar rapid course. The experienced aquarist is able to spot an ailing fish at a glance, but it is important to separate each of the signs and symptoms of illness in order to arrive at the right diagnosis. Are rapid respirations shallow and fast, or the deep heavy type? Is the fish scratching his side or his operculum? One must learn to be a critical observer and differentiate such signs. Such a large body of misconceptions regarding the care and treatment of aquarium fish has accumulated, that these misconceptions have become a major obstruction to a rational approach to treatment. One cannot effectively use this manual and yet hang on to many of the false notions promulgated by some of the recent general books on keeping salt water fish. For example, it is not true that *Cryptocaryon* (salt water Ich) will die out if a tank is left unoccupied for three days, or for that matter, for one week. It is not true that some amount of scratching is normal. Healthy fish probably never scratch.

It is useless to add a prescribed number of drops of copper sulfate to a tank containing coral, shells, or undergravel filter and expect to attain a therapeutic copper level. Most of it will be removed within hours from solution. Similarly, an activated carbon filter will rapidly remove most medications from the tank. It is not true that "disease introduced or appearing in a well balanced tank will usually clear up with a minimum of loss naturally compared to medicinal treatment of the whole tank". It is not true that "if marine fish are kept very healthy and well fed in a tank for months or years they will become resistant to infectious organisms that may be added with new specimens". And it is ludicrous and self-defeating to assert that usually the "cure" is worse than the disease. The disease problem may be staggering but we must at least *try* to cure them.

In addition to the common diseases covered in this manual, there are a great many that are encountered occasionally. They are purposely omitted in order to emphasize the real problem

4

diseases for which a system of treatment has been developed. Furthermore, many of the unusual diseases will be coincidentally cured by the cleansing treatment used for the common diseases.

Not all diseases are caused by infectious agents. Some are due to toxins, chemical pollutants, heavy metals including copper used in treatment, insecticides, and many others. These can only be controlled by careful attention to water quality. Other diseases in this category are caused by malnutrition, such as fatty degeneration of the liver and scoliosis of the spine. An adequate mixed diet that contains protein as well as carbohydrate, is low in animal fats, and with supplemental vitamins should control such nutritional problems in most fish.

While it is the purpose of this manual to present a system of treatment of the common infectious diseases of exotic marine fish, newer drugs, devices and techniques undoubtedly will call for changes in treatment schedules and possibly some day, in the entire approach to this problem. Our understanding of most of the diseases we seek to cure is only fragmentary. One scientist may spend many years or a lifetime working out the life cycle of a single protozoan parasite, and the number of workers in this field are relatively few, so that revolutionary cures should not be expected. Yet there is a great opportunity for the aquarist to make a contribution in this field by keeping a careful record of treatments, successes and failures, and by innovation. But this should always be done scientifically with adequate numbers of test animals and controls, and by careful control of variables.

2. THE DIAGNOSIS

Cleansing treatment does not require a specific diagnosis, but as amplified in the introduction, all new or wild fish require cleansing treatment to eliminate the disease carrier state. Occasionally, however, a new fish will be received in a shipment very ill. Such a fish should be treated separately by the cleansing method, and if a diagnosis can be made, then it should be treated specifically for that disease. For aid in diagnosis consult the Diagnostic Key — Solitary Fish.

On receipt of a new shipment of fish by air freight or any other form of transport, the fish will have spent many hours in plastic bags with relatively little water. They will frequently be found breathing rapidly and this is usually due to one of three conditions: high ammonia level in the water, low O_2 tension, or bacterial disease. In the case of high ammonia levels, the source of ammonia is the excretion of nitrogenous wastes into the water by the gills and the urine of the fish. Ammonia is the principal form of such excretion in fishes[1].

Ammonia is present in the water in two forms: the ionized (NH_4+) and the un-ionized state (NH_3). Only the un-ionized state is toxic to fish[2] and this exists in greater proportion in water that has a high pH (seawater 8.3-8.5) than a low pH (freshwater 7.0)[3]. This is undoubtedly one reason freshwater fish can survive long delays in shipment better than saltwater fish. Furthermore, a decrease in dissolved oxygen in the water increases the toxicity of un-ionized ammonia (NH_3). Therefore, the first step in care for fish received in shipment is to put them in a large volume of new water at the same pH and temperature. The

1. Wood, J. D.: Nitrogen Excretion in Some Marine Teleosts. Canadian J. Biochem. Physiol. 36: 1237-1242, 1958.
2. Milne, M. D., Scribner, B. H., Crawford, M. A.: Non-ionic Diffusion and the Excretion of Weak Acids and Bases, Amer. J. Med. 24: 709-729, 1958.
3. Downing, K. M., Merkens, J. C.: The Influence of Dissolved Oxygen Concentration on the Toxicity of Un-ionized Ammonia to Rainbow Trout (Salmo giardnerii Richardson), Ann. Apl. Biol. 43: 243-246, 1955.

water from which they are removed should not be added to the new water as it may be teeming with bacteria and other pathogenic organisms. High nitrite levels are also toxic but are not a consideration at this point because the ammonia wastes are only converted to nitrite by nitrifying bacteria, which are found only in the established tank with a biologic filter.

After a shipment of fish has been received, transferred to a hospital tank with clean water and the cleansing treatment begun, the Diagnostic Key will be helpful in following their course. If the hospital tank contains several fish, use the key designed for the community tank, otherwise use the key for solitary fish.

DIAGNOSTIC KEYS

Directions for use:

1. Always start at the beginning: 1-a.

2. If the first statement is true, go to the line indicated at the right hand margin of the page. In the Solitary Fish Key, for example, line 1-a says "Rapid breathing". If the fish displays this characteristic, go to line 3 and read 3-a.

3. If the first statement does not apply, go to part "b". For example, in the Solitary Fish Key, if 1-a is not true because the fish does not display rapid breathing, go to 1-b "Normal or slow breathing". This is the only alternative, and must apply. You are directed to go to 2. Read line 2-a. If this applies, go to line 9-a; if not, then the statement in line 2-b must be correct and you must proceed to line 14.

4. Discipline is required in progressing through the key. Do not allow yourself to jump or skip unless specifically directed to do so. Do not search the key for a single symptom. A diagnosis derived in this way will frequently be erroneous. Always start with 1-a and progress as directed through the key.

DIAGNOSTIC KEY — Solitary Fish
(To be used only when no other fish are present in tank)

1-a	Rapid breathing	3
b	Normal or slow breathing	2
2-a	Skin (including fins) has ulcer, spots, cotton wool lesions, nodules, cloudy appearance or raised scales	9

b	Skin clear, no lesions	14
3-a	Skin has ulcer, spots, cotton wool lesions, nodules, cloudy appearance or raised scales	4
b	Skin clear, no lesions	11
4-a	Skin has raised scales and often faded colors	Tuberculosis
b	Skin has other lesions	5
5-a	Skin is covered with fine dust-like lesions that are white, tan or gray and pin-point size	Oodinium
b	Skin has other lesions	6
6-a	Skin has many or numerous pin-head sized white spots	Cryptocaryon
b	Skin has other lesions	7
7-a	Skin has ulcer or ulcers, white patch, or lateral line lesions	Bacterial infection
b	Skin has other lesions	8
8-a	Skin has numerous minute ulcers ...	Cryptocaryon
b	Skin has other lesions	10
9-a	Skin has one or rarely several gray, smooth, lumpy nodules	Lymphocystis
b	Skin has cotton wool lesions	Saprolegnia
10-a	Fins have many pin-head sized white spots	Cryptocaryon
b	Fins are clear or have other lesions ..	Bacterial infection
11-a	Fins have many pin-head sized white spots	Cryptocaryon
b	Fins are clear or have other lesions ..	12
12-a	Fins have a cloudy or milky thickened appearance	Bacterial infection
b	Fins clear or have other lesions	13
13-a	Fins are very ragged or frayed	15
b	Fins are clear or have other lesions ..	23
14-a	Fins are ragged or frayed	Ichthyophonus
b	Fins clear or have other lesions	17
15-a	Eyes have a white film or clouded appearance	Bacterial infection

b	Eyes clear or have other lesions	16
16-a	Exophthalmos — one or both eyes protrude abnormally	Tuberculosis
b	Eyes show no exophthalmos	22
17-a	Exophthalmos	Ichthyophonus
b	Eyes show no exophthalmos	19
18-a	Fish is listless	20
b	Fish is not listless, showing normal or hyperactive movement	21
19-a	Fish is listless	Ichthyophonus
b	Fish is not listless, showing normal or hyperactive movement	Intestinal trematodes
20-a	Fish displays jerking or twitching movements	Ichthyophonus
b	Fish moves normally	Oodinium Tuberculosis High nitrite level Bacterial infection Ichthyphonus
21-a	Fish lying on bottom, often tilted to one side (Go to 21-b if fish is obviously dying or behavior is normal)	Oodinium Bacterial infection
b	Fish do not show this symptom	Bacterial infection High nitrite level
22-a	Fish is scratching on coral or bottom	21
b	Fish is not scratching	18
23-a	Fins are deteriorated with protruding rays or are reduced to stubs	Bacterial infection
b	Fins are clear or have other lesions ..	24
24-a	Eyes have a white film or clouded appearance	Bacterial infection
b	Eyes clear or have other lesions	25
25-a	Exophthalmos — one or both eyes protrude abnormally	Ichthyphonus

b	Eyes show no exophthalmos	26
26-a	Fish is scratching on coral or bottom..	27
b	Fish is not scratching	28
27-a	Fish is listless	31
b	Fish is not listless, showing normal or hyperactive movement	Oodinium Gill flukes Bacterial infection High nitrite level
28-a	Fish is listless	29
b	Fish is not listless, showing normal or hyperactive movement	High nitrite level Bacterial infection
29-a	Fish displays jerking or twitching movements	Ichthyophonus
b	Fish moves normally	30
30-a	Vertigo — fish shows loss of balance	Ichthyophonus
b	Fish does not show signs of loss of equilibrium	Oodinium Bacterial infection High nitrite level
31-a	Fish lying on bottom, often tilted to one side (Go to 31-b if fish is obviously dying or this is normal behavior)	Bacterial infection
b	Fish do not show this symptom or it is normal	High nitrite level Bacterial infection

DIAGNOSTIC KEY — Community Tank

1-a	All or most of the fish in the tank are sick or show an abnormally increased breathing rate	22
b	Only one or rarely two fish are sick ..	2
2-a	Rapid breathing	3

11

b	Normal or slow breathing	23
3-a	Skin has ulcer, spots, cotton wool lesions, nodule, cloudy appearance or raised scales	15
b	Skin is clear, no lesions	26
4-a	Skin has raised scales and often faded colors	Tuberculosis
b	Skin has other lesions	Bacterial infection
5-a	Skin is covered with fine dust-like lesions that are white, tan or gray and pin-point size	Oodinium
b	Skin has other lesions	6
6-a	Skin has many or numerous pin-head size white spots	Cryptocaryon
b	Skin has other lesions	7
7-a	Skin has ulcer or ulcers, white patch or lateral line lesions	Bacterial infection
b	Skin has other lesions	8
8-a	Skin has numerous minute ulcers ...	Cryptocaryon
b	Skin has other lesions	10
9-a	Skin has one or rarely several gray smooth lumpy nodules	Lymphocystis
b	Skin has cotton wool lesions	Saprolegnia
10-a	Fins have many white pin-head size spots	Cryptocaryon
b	Fins are clear or have other lesions ..	11
11-a	Fins have a cloudy or milky thickened appearance	Bacterial infection
b	Fins are clear or have other lesions ..	13
12-a	Fins are ragged or frayed	29
b	Fins are clear or have other lesions ..	33
13-a	Fins are deteriorated with protruding rays or are reduced to stubs	Bacterial infection
b	Fins are clear or have other lesions ..	14
14-a	Eyes have a white film or clouded appearance	Bacterial infection
b	Eyes clear or have other lesions	20

15-a	Exophthalmos — one or both eyes protrude abnormally	Tuberculosis
b	Eyes show no exophthalmos	4
16-a	Fish is scratching on coral or bottom	Bacterial infection
b	Fish is not scratching	17
17-a	Fish is listless	21
b	Fish not listless showing normal or hyperactive movement	Bacterial infection
18-a	Fish displays jerking or twitching movements	Ichthyophonus
b	Fish moves normally	20
19-a	Fish lying on bottom, often tilted to one side. (Go to 19-b if fish is obviously dying or this is normal behavior for the species)	Bacterial infection
b	Fish do not show this symptom or it is normal	Bacterial infection and Cryptocaryon
20-a	Vertigo — Fish shows loss of balance..	Ichthyophonus
b	Fish does not show signs of loss of equilibrium	Tuberculosis or Ichthyophonus
21-a	Abdomen has a sunken or pinched appearance	Tuberculosis
b	Abdomen appears normal or slightly protruding	Tuberculosis or Bacterial infection
22-a	Skin has ulcer, spots, cotton wool lesions, nodules, cloudy appearance or raised scales	5
b	Skin is clear, no lesions	25
23-a	Skin has ulcer, spots, cotton wool lesions, nodules, cloudy appearance or raised scales	9
b	Skin is clear, no lesions	27
24-a	Fins have many white pin-head	

	size spots	Cryptocaryon
b	Fins are clear or have other lesions ..	25
25-a	Fins have a cloudy or milky thickened appearance	Bacterial infection
b	Fins are clear or have other lesions ..	28
26-a	Fins have a cloudy or milky thickened appearance	Bacterial infection
b	Fins are clear or have other lesions ..	12
27-a	Fins are ragged or frayed	Ichthyophonus
b	Fins are clear or have other lesions ..	35
28-a	Fins are deteriorated with protruding rays or are reduced to stubs	Bacterial infection
b	Fins are clear or have other lesions ..	30
29-a	Fins are deteriorated with protruding rays or are reduced to stubs	32
b	Fins are clear or have other lesions ..	31
30-a	Eyes have a white film or clouded appearance	Bacterial infection
b	Eyes clear or other lesions	44
31-a	Eyes have a white film or cloudy appearance	Bacterial infection
b	Eyes clear or have other lesions	37
32-a	Eyes have a white film or cloudy appearance	Bacterial infection
b	Eyes clear or have other lesions	34
33-a	Eyes have a white film or cloudy appearance	Bacterial infection
b	Eyes clear or have other lesions	36
34-a	Exophthalmos — one or both eyes protrude abnormally	Tuberculosis
b	Eyes show no exophthalmos	16
35-a	Exophthalmos — one or both eyes protrude abnormally	Ichthyophonus
b	Eyes show no exophthalmos	41
36-a	Exophthalmos — one or both	

	eyes protrude abnormally	Ichthyophonus
b	Eyes show no exophthalmos	38
37-a	Exophthalmos — one or both eyes protrude abnormally	18
b	Eyes show no exophthalmos	42
38-a	Fish is scratching on coral or bottom..	39
b	Fish is not scratching	40
39-a	Fish is listless	Bacterial infection
b	Fish not listless showing normal or hyperactive movement	Gill flukes Bacterial infection
40-a	Fish is listless	43
b	Fish not listless showing normal or hyperactive movement	Bacterial infection
41-a	Fish is listless	Ichthyophonus
b	Fish is not listless showing normal or hyperactive movement	Intestinal trematodes
42-a	Fish displays jerking or twitching movement	Ichthyophonus
b	Fish moves normally	45
43-a	Fish displays jerking or twitching movements	Ichthyophonus
b	Fish moves normally	46
44-a	Fish lying on the bottom, often tilted to one side. (Go to 44-b if fish is obviously dying or this is normal behavior for the species)	Oodinium Bacterial infection
b	Fish do not show this symptom or it is normal	Oodinium High nitrite level Bacterial infection
45-a	Vertigo — fish shows loss of balance..	Ichthyphonus
b	Fish does not show signs of loss of equilibrium	Tuberculosis or Ichthyophonus

46-a   Vertigo — fish shows loss of balance.. Ichthyophonus
   b   Fish does not show signs of loss
       of equilibrium 47
47-a   Abdomen has a sunken or
       pinched appearance .... Ichthyophonus
   b   Abdomen appears normal or
       slightly protruding .... Ichthyophonus
                                                Bacterial
                                                infection

3. CLEANSING TREATMENT

The purpose of the cleansing treatment is to eliminate disease in the carrier state, particularly *Oodinium, Cryptocaryon*, pathogenic bacteria, tuberculosis, gill flukes, and *Trichodina*. These agents are extremely common in wild fishes and it is best to assume that the fish carry them and treat the fish initially rather than wait for them to proliferate exponentially in the confines of the aquarium. Fish having obvious ulcers, severe tail rot or fungus disease will require additional treatment after the cleansing.

Needless to say, the water that is used in treatment should be free from bacteria and parasites. The use of artificial seawater will fulfill this requirement. If natural seawater is used, it should be sterilized by the addition of chlorine. The use of 50 ppm of free chlorine $(Cl-)$ is a recommended level[4]. Alternatively 1 tsp. of household Clorox (5.25% sodium hypochlorite) per gallon has been found satisfactory. Swimming pool chlorine (sodium hypochlorite) is more concentrated, cheaper, and available in liquid or dry powder form. Regardless of the quantity added, it must all be neutralized after a minimum of six hours by the addition of sodium thiosulfate $(Na_2S_2O_3)$. This is also known as "hypo", available at any photographic supply store. A simple chlorine test kit such as that used for swimming pools is adequate to check for the absence of residual chlorine. The water can be used as soon as the chlorine has been completely neutralized(double check by smell). A less satisfactory preparation of seawater is water that has been cycled through a diatom filter for 24 hours and then allowed to stand in the dark for at least two weeks. While in theory, diatomaceous earth filtration is capable of removing protozoan parasites and bacteria, in practice there is often sufficient reflux or leakage in the filter barrier to allow the passage of some organisms and this method of treatment

4. Spotte, S. H.: Fish and Invertebrate Culture, Pub. John Wiley & Sons, Inc., 1970, p. 113.

alone is insufficient. Ultraviolet light sterilization is capable of removing up to 99% of bacteria from the circulating water and in this regard is useful. It may not, however, remove all the organisms of *Oodinium* and *Cryptocaryon*. The effects of ozone are similar and until further proof of the efficiency of ultraviolet light and ozone becomes available, their use alone cannot be recommended with confidence.

Preparation for Treatment:

First prepare tanks as follows:

1. Hospital tanks. These are bare 3-5 gallon tanks or plastic trays. The number required will depend upon the number of fish to be treated. Approximately five small fish/gallon or two medium fish/gallon is maximum and glass or plastic hiding places should be provided and occasionally plastic separators to prevent fin nipping by incompatible fish. Add one air stone to each tank and provide moderate aeration. The following medications are then added: copper sulfate to 0.15 ppm, (the number of drops required to achieve this level should be indicated on the label. If not, the proper level must be determined with your copper test kit), chloramphenicol 50 mg/gal., neomycin 250 mg/gal., isoniazid 40 mg/gal.

2. Established Tank. To any tank having an established biological filter add copper sulfate to a level of 0.3 ppm. This step will insure complete eradication of *Oodinium*. Then add quinacrine hydrochloride, 8-12 mg/gal. This will kill *Cryptocaryon*, many sporozans, and other ciliates affecting the gills such as *Henneguaya*. Avoid strong light and keep overhead aquarium light off as light will gradually inactivate the quinacrine hydrochloride.

Most of the drugs mentioned in this book can be obtained from your local veterinarian.

While there is a wide safety margin in dosage of antibiotics, great care is needed in achieving the correct dose for the antimalarial class of drugs used. This includes quinacrine, primaquine, chloroquine and pyrimethamine. As marketed, these drugs show considerable strength variations between manufacturerers lots.

Unless the medication is purchased specifically for

18

aquarium use from a reliable distributor indicating that bio-assay has been performed, the indicated dosage should not be trusted.

For example, pyrimethamine from one bottle may be optimally effective at 8 mg/gal., but the same dose from another bottle may be found to be toxic. The aquarist may conduct his own bio-assay to arrive at the maximum tolerable dose by treating several small healthy fish at severe dosages for one week. Approximately ½ the minimum lethal dose will usually be a satisfactory treatment level.

Another very important principle in the use of the anti-malarial drugs is to accurately measure the number of gallons of water to be treated in order to avoid an overdosage or an ineffectual underdose. The water capacity of a tank is easily ascertained by multiplying the width, height, and length of the water column (in inches) in the tank, and dividing the result by 231. The result of such an exercise is often surprisingly different from the advertised capacity of the tank. Remember also that the gravel occupies space, so your depth measurement should be taken from the top surface of the gravel to the actual top surface of the water.

Method of Treatment:

1. Equalize the temperature and pH of the water in which the fish are received with water in the bare hospital tanks or trays.
2. Transfer the fish to the hospital tanks or trays, preferably by hand to avoid damage to the fish.
3. Cover the hospital tanks or trays completely or several fish will surely jump out the moment your back is turned.
4. The treatment period is two days. Do not feed for 24 hours, then feed flake food very sparingly once a day.
5. At the end of two days (48 hours) transfer the fish to 10-20 gallon tanks having established biological filters (under-gravel), air stone, copper level of 0.25 to 0.3 ppm and quinacrine. Begin regular feeding twice a day. The copper and quinacrine levels must be maintained for 10 days, at the end of which time the fish may be transferred to any permanent tank or they may remain in these tanks.

SUMMARY — CLEANSING TREATMENT

Preparation

1. Hospital tank or tray: add copper to 0.15 ppm, chloramphenicol 50 mg/gal., neomycin 250 mg/gal., isoniazid 40 mg/gal.
2. Established tank with biological filter: add copper to 0.3 ppm, quinacrine hydrochloride 8-12 mg/gal.*

DAY 1

1. Equalize water temperature and pH.
2. Transfer to hospital tank or tray. Do not feed.

DAY 2

Feed flake food sparingly one time.

DAY 3

Transfer to established tank with copper and quinacrine level. Treat for 10 days and feed normally. Avoid strong light. The yellow coloration of the water may be removed now with activated carbon filtration. Normal fish coloration will return slowly.

---

* Dosage determined in bio-assay — this is available in bio-assayed form from Global Marine, P.O. Box 6611, St. Petersburg, Fla. 33736

4. SELECTIVE TREATMENT

OODINIUM OCELLATUM

Fish infected with this organism will usually have a white, tan, golden, or gray dusty or powdery appearance of the skin which is diffuse over the head and sides as well as the fins. (Plate 1)

This powdery appearance is very difficult to see, requiring very close inspection and incident light at an angle. When seen, this is a late stage of the infection. The gill filaments are the primary site of infection, and therefore the fish always show rapid breathing as an initial symptom.

In the absence of rapid breathing, the fish are not suffering from Oodinium. Rapid breathing is generally unmistakable, being very fast or panting and shallow. At least to the extent of rapid breathing, *all* the fish in the tank will be affected to varying degrees. The course of the disease is very rapid, and from the time when fast breathing is noted to death it is usually no more than two to four days.

Generally, before the appearance of dust-like skin lesions, the fish will be seen scratching on coral, bottom, or rocks and will be hyperactive with darting and dashing movements. As their condition deteriorates they will remain at an angle to the surface, panting, and later they may be found lying on the bottom panting and exhausted. The powdery appearance may now be visible. At this late stage they are terminal and treatment will usually fail.

The first step in treatment is a freshwater bath, if the fish can be caught easily. Freshwater rapidly enters the cell of the *Oodinium* organism expanding it by osmotic pressure until it ruptures. Most fish can withstand the sudden hydrostatic change for periods of 10 to 30 minutes without any apparent long term adverse effects, but two minutes is sufficient to elimi-nate all exposed *Oodinium* organisms. The bath is prepared by placing 1 - 5 gal. of tapwater in a suitable bare container. Add sodium thiosulfate, 1 drop per gal., to remove any chlorine, or use water that has been vigorously aerated for one to two days. Next check the pH and be sure it is the same as your salt water. If it is too acid, add a pinch of household baking soda (sodium bicarbonate) and check again. It is very important that the pH is the same as the seawater, if it varies by more than 0.2, the fish may show signs of shock. Some organisms may remain inaccessible in the gills, possibly protected by mucous, so that subsequent treatment with copper is necessary. The copper can be administered in the form of copper sulfate, copper acetate, citrated copper sulfate, or copper-formalin. Dinospores are relativity insensitive to levels of copper under 0.25 ppm and 24 to 36 hours are required to kill them. Fish are also quite sensitive to copper and the margin of safety is extremely narrow. The optimal treatment level of copper is 0.3 ppm for ten days. A level of 0.5 ppm for this period of time may have severe toxic effects on the fish, and a level of less than 0.25 ppm may not completely eradicate the disease. If there is to be a recurrence, it is generally on about the sixth to eighth day indicating that a few dinospores survived inadequate initial treatment. An interval of about seven days is required for completion of the life cycle ending in the release of hundreds of new infective motile dinospores. This can only happen when the copper level is too low.

For purposes of treatment, all fish must be removed from the aquarium and placed in a hospital tank having no coral, carbon filter or shells. Only silica gravel is allowed. All calcareous objects remove the copper rapidly from solution and an adequate treatment level is difficult to achieve. The required amount of copper is then added and preferably checked with a copper test kit for a level of 0.3 ppm. This level should be built up in at least two stages because fish that are already having respiratory difficulty produce copious amounts of mucous from the gills in response to a high level of copper and may suffocate. Furthermore, juveniles of certain species of fish appear to be more sensitive to copper, such as puffers, spiny boxfish and mandarins, which have highly developed mucous gland secretion in the skin as a primary defense mechanism. Other fish that have no scales and depend on a mucous coat for protection may have a similar reaction to copper. Symptoms of copper toxicity are extremely slow respirations and listlessness or lying on the bottom.

While it is said that some fish may carry *Oodinium* organisms in few numbers and not show any signs of illness, no dormant or resting stage separate from the fish has been described and therefore it is theoretically possible to rid a tank of the infection by removing all fish for a certain period of time. This period has not been accurately determined, but several experiments by the author have demonstrated that infective dinoflagellates of at least one strain are present in tanks that have remained free of fish or invertebrates for four weeks, but were absent after eight weeks at 78° F.

The fact that it is possible for invertebrates to carry the organisms and introduce them to aquaria has been demonstrated by the author. Even when assorted invertebrates including gorgonians, star fish, sea urchins and sponges had been quarantined for three days with continuous diatom filtering of the water, they were infective. *Oodinium* probably does not feed or complete its life cycle on invertebrates, but this has not been proven. Since most invertebrates are killed by copper, it appears that the only solution for eliminating *Oodinium* from invertebrates at this stage in our knowledge are the fresh water bath or a long period of quarantine.

To treat the coral-decorated infected tank from which the fish were taken, remove all invertebrates, allow the undergravel filter to continue operating and proceed to treat the tank with large doses of copper. Add approximately 30 times the dosage of copper recommended for a bare tank. Be sure the activated carbon filter is removed and if siphon tubes connect to it, they should be emptied. At the end of six days, the recharged activated carbon filter is started, and the fish can be added on the seventh day, provided the copper level is below 0.4 ppm.

Should the decision be made to treat the diseased fish in the primary tank because it is impossible to catch and remove them, then all invertebrates must first be removed. Remove all activated carbon filters and add air stones for supplemental air as needed. A tank fully decorated with coral may require 20-50 times as much copper as a bare tank of equal volume if it has not had previous copper treatment. Add copper sulfate or copper acetate to a measured level of approximately 0.3 ppm the first day. On the second day the level in a tank containing coral and undergravel filter will be down to 0.05 ppm or less and additional copper will have to be added to a measured level of approximately 0.4 ppm. On the third day additional copper will have to be added to a measured level of 0.4 ppm. This level may hold for several days but must be monitored daily and not allowed to drop below 0.2 ppm until seven days have elapsed. Then allow the level to gradually fall without adding copper, or start the activated carbon filter after it has been cleaned with fresh water and recharged with carbon. Most of the copper will be rapidly removed.

No other treatment for *Oodinium* has yet been found to be as effective as copper. Malachite green is very toxic to small fish and in therapeutic doses frequently kills them. Large fish may survive, but the efficacy of treatment is not well established. Acriflavine or trypaflavine appear to damage the slime coating of the skin and may make the fish more vulnerable to bacterial infections. They also are not very effective against *Oodinium*. Methylene blue has the advantage of aiding respiration by acting as an oxygen carrier similar to hemoglobin when present in plasma, and it is moderately effective against *Oodinium*, but treatment is more prolonged and the author has experienced recurrences. It is possible that a combination of methylene blue to aid respiration and copper would be effective but no information is available on this modification of treatment.

Oodinium

---

1. Treat early — as soon as the diagnosis is suspected. DO NOT DELAY.
2. Prepare hospital tank: Add water, air stone and 0.15 ppm of copper to a bare tank.

DAY 1

1. Give all fish two minutes freshwater bath (See page 21).
2. Place fish in hospital tank.
3. Aerate moderately. Do not feed.
4. Stop activated carbon filter in established tank from which the fish were taken, remove filter from

the tank and clean it. Continue biological filtration (under-gravel filter).

5. Add 10 times the drops/gal. required to achieve a level of 0.3 ppm of copper to the original established tank. (All invertebrates must be removed to a separate container of adequate size. Give two minute bath in freshwater before placing in new seawater).

DAY 2

1. Add the other ½ dose of the copper medication to the hospital tank. The level should now be 0.3 ppm.
2. Add 10 times the dose/gal. of copper medication to the original tank.
3. Feed flake food to fish sparingly.

DAY 3

1. Add 10 times the dose/gal. of copper medication to the original tank.
2. Feed flake food to fish sparingly.

DAY 4

1. Check copper level in the original tank. If less than 0.25 ppm add 10 times the dose/gal. of copper medication.
2. Feed flake food sparingly.

DAY 5

1. Check copper level in original tank. If level has stabilized between 0.4 and 0.25 ppm, fish may be returned. If level is less than 0.25 ppm, add 10 times the dose/gal. of copper medication. Leave fish in the hospital tank.
2. Feed flake food to fish sparingly.

```
┌─────────────────────────────────────────────┐
│                    DAY 6                      │
│  1. Check copper level in the original tank. If too low, │
│     add 10 times the dose/gal. of copper medication. If  │
│     above 0.4 ppm, start the recharged activated car-    │
│     bon filter.                                          │
│  2. Return fish to original established home tank, if    │
│     not already done, when the copper level has          │
│     stabilized at 0.25-0.3 ppm.                          │
│  3. Resume feeding.                                      │
└─────────────────────────────────────────────┘
```

```
┌─────────────────────────────────────────────┐
│                    DAY 10                     │
│  1. Start activated carbon filter.                       │
└─────────────────────────────────────────────┘
```

```
┌─────────────────────────────────────────────┐
│                    DAY 20                     │
│  1. Return invertebrates to established original home    │
│     tank after two minute bath in fresh water. Do not    │
│     contaminate the original tank with any salt water    │
│     from the invertebrate container.                     │
└─────────────────────────────────────────────┘
```

CRYPTOCARYON IRRITANS

Fish infected with this organism will usually have from 5 to 10 or many white to grayish-white spots that will first be seen on the fins and later noticed all over the body. (Plate 2, 3).

The spots are small, somewhat smaller than the size of a pin-head but not dust-like as seen in *Oodinium*. Furthermore, the spots are always discrete and seldom confluent, so that they will be sharp like a period (.) and about the same size. In this disease, the skin is affected first, but later the organisms will infiltrate the gill filaments and will eventually invade the blood vessels of the gills. (Plate 19).

Furthermore, in advanced stages of the disease the trophonts will ulcerate and infiltrate the skin (Plate 4) and reside beneath the epidermis where they are not as readily exposed to medication in the water. This is the reason for some recurrences after treatment.

Also, fish that secrete a protective mucous coat may be particularly difficult to cure because the mucous prevents drug penetration. Surgeon fish, mandarins and spiny boxfish are three such examples. The breathing rate is increased except in the very earliest stages when perhaps only one or two spots are present on one fin. But as soon as there is any appreciable degree of infection, the fish will exhibit rapid breathing. It usually does not reach the stage of panting or extremely shallow rapid breathing as seen in *Oodinium*. In perhaps half of the cases the fish will exhibit scratching, but this is not done with the frequency and violence seen in *Oodinium* infections. In late stages of *Cryptocaryon* infection, the fins will show deterioration with fraying and then some uneven reduction in size. Some of this fin necrosis may be due to secondary bacterial infection consequent to damage by the *Cryptocaryon*.

Treatment:

Fish should be left in the infected tank and treated with 8-12 mg/gal.* of quinacrine hydrochloride. Certain invertebrates appear to be injured by this medication, particularly anemones and live coral which should be removed from the tank and placed in quarantine for approximately two to three weeks. Other invertebrates such as sponges, gorgonians, coral banded shrimp, feather dusters, starfish, spiral tube worms, crabs, sea urchins, and live shells appear to be resistant to the drug and can be left in the tank. The under-gravel filter and air stones should be left in operation, but any activated carbon filters should be removed, cleaned, but not restarted until the termination of the treatment.

The activated carbon will rapidly remove all free quinacrine from the water, but the fish and invertebrates will retain the medication for a week or two as evidenced by a slight yellow tinge. The slow elimination of this medication from the fish is helpful in preventing recurrences. During the period of treatment, lighting should be reduced by turning out the overhead lights on the tank and avoiding direct sunlight. This is because quinacrine is slowly inactivated by light. Treatment should last 10 days before starting activated carbon filtration.

An alternative treatment that is probably equally effective

---

*Toxic reactions are rapid breathing, loss of appetite, vertigo, or loss of equilibrium and lying on bottom. See page 18. Only that dosage derived by bio-assay can be trusted implicitly.

and may be used in the occasional case where the *Cryptocaryon* organism has been found to be resistant to quinacrine, is the combination of chloroquine (40 mg/gal.) and primaquine (15 mg/gal.). In this case prolonged treatment may result in dark pigmentation of the fish, but this will resolve after treatment has been terminated by activated carbon filtration.

Pyrimethamine (4-8 mg/gal.*) is also useful in the treatment of *Cryptocaryon* and can be used in combination with chloroquine or primaquine. All of these drugs are for the treatment of malaria in humans and affect different stages in the life cycle of the malaria organism. Chloroquine is the fastest acting, and while a similar relative rate of action against *Cryptocaryon* has not been definitely proven it may be so, and for this reason is included in combination therapy. Providing adequate activated carbon filtration is initiated after the course of treatment, it is not necessary to change the water. It is not sufficient to simply stop a carbon filter for a period of treatment and then restart it as there is a high probability of reintroduction of *Cryptocaryon* into the tank and reinfection from the filter. Such filters should be cleaned with fresh water and recharged before starting.

When infected fish are removed from a tank and treated, but the tank remains untreated, recurrences have been noted after return of the fish on the sixth to ninth day. This is because cysts that had dropped from the fish to the bottom, developed and released their tomites. This conflicts with the notion advanced in some books that a tank can be freed of these parasites by removing the fish for three days. While it may be true that the very active tomites will die in 36 to 48 hours if a host is not found, it is necessary to add at least nine days to this period to account for asexual reproduction in the cyst. A quarantine period of two weeks is therefore recommended for the natural elimination of the parasite from a tank known to have contained infected fish and that cannot be treated by medications. This situation pertains particularly for invertebrates such as gorgonians, urchins, tube worms and live coral which should never be added to an established tank without such quarantine because they have been known to carry *Cryptocaryon*, as well as *Oodinium* when newly collected. If the fish are to be removed from the tank for

*Dosage determined by bio-assay. Toxic reactions are marked darkening of the colors and death with open gaping mouth. The correct dosage is ½ the dose at which early toxic signs occur. See page 18.

treatment, they will benefit greatly from a two minute fresh water bath (see page 21), which will kill most of the *Cryptocaryon* organisms immediately, leaving only those embedded in mucous or buried in the gill filaments or beneath scales. The bath should be followed by a full course of treatment with quinacrine.

Many other medications have been tested and are considered less effective than those recommended. These include quinine sulfate, chlorite, acriflavine, sulfaquinine, malachite green, copper sulfate, methylene blue, potassium permanganate, metronidazole, and many antibiotics.

Cryptocaryon

1. Treat all fish in their established tank.
2. Remove activated carbon filter, recharge it, but do not restart.
3. Continue biological filtration (under-gravel filter).
4. Add air stone if needed.
5. Reduce lighting.
6. Add 4-6 mg/gal. of quinacrine hydrochloride directly to the tank.
7. Add 4-6 mg/gal. of quinacrine hydrochloride in 24 hours.
8. Terminate treatment after 10 days by restarting activated carbon filter.

TUBERCULOSIS

The usual causitive organism is *Mycobacteria marinum*, a different species from that which causes human tuberculosis. It can, however, cause a localized granulomatous infection in humans if inoculated by an infected fish spine.

The signs and symptoms of infected fish are first rapid breathing. Since the course of the disease is usually slow, the fish may display very rapid breathing for weeks. They may continue to eat but will eventually hide a great deal of the time and finally stop eating. During this period, the fins will become progressively more ragged, and the colors faded. Small groups of raised scales will appear on the sides and the skin coloration may acquire a blotchy appearance. The fish has a "moth-eaten" appearance. (Plate 5).

As the gills become progressively infected the fish may spend considerable time just beneath the surface, poised at an angle, breathing fast. While in the beginning when the fish is still eating, it may be hyperactive, eventually it will become listless remaining in one spot or resting on the bottom. Exophthalmos, or bulging out of one or both eyes, is a more or less frequent sign. (Plate 6). Ulcers of the skin are occasionally seen; these are deep with ragged margins. Finally, the fish's abdomen will appear sunken and acquire a pinched look and he will become progressively weak and finally die. Usually only one fish in a tank has outward signs of infection at one time, but over a period of months several fish may drop off from this disease. There appears to be a strong natural resistance in fish, and not all of the fish exposed will necessarily acquire the disease. Occasionally all the fish in a tank or new shipment will suffer acute infection from *Mycobacterium* and will show very shallow rapid breathing and listlessness. They will die in one to two weeks. The diagnosis of acute tuberculosis is made on the basis of these symptoms, and the lack of response to treatment for *Oodinium* and bacterial disease.

Treatment:

A combination of antibiotics is indicated in the treatment of tuberculosis because the agent may be resistant to any single antibiotic unless it is chosen on the basis of elaborate sensitivity studies which are not feasible in the case of the particular fish one wishes to save. Based on limited studies, the preferred drugs are rifampin, streptomycin and cycloserine. Isoniazid is sometimes helpful and may be added to the water in addition to administration in the food. Antibiotic sensitivity studies show inhibition of growth in culture by rifampin and streptomycin fairly consistently. Ethionamide and cycloserine may be useful but occasional resistant strains make these drugs unreliable unless used in combination with other drugs or after they have been shown to be effective by sensitivity studies. These last two antibiotics should be given in the food.

Rifampin is not soluble in water, and can only be administered in the food. It should be added at the rate of 6 mg/100 g of food. Cycloserine can be added to food at the rate of 3 mg/100 g, and being soluble in water, it can be added to the tank 50 mg/gal. Streptomycin can be added to the water at the rate of 40 mg/gal.

Since the disease is infectious in a tank, it is desirable to leave the sick fish in the tank and feed all the fish medicated food. Ultraviolet sterilization of the water may help prevent spread to other fish. If, however, the fish has the disease in an advanced stage and is no longer eating, he should be removed to a hospital tank and treated separately. In this case the antibiotics should be added to the water and, if there is improvement to the point where the fish begins eating again, the medication should be given in the food. It should be given only once a day, preferably in the morning so the food can remain in the tank for several hours while the fish, with understandably poor appetite, picks at it. The evening meal can be eliminated until the appetite returns. When this happens, provide the necessary variety by using flake food. Treatment should last at least two weeks.

This is a difficult disease to treat and if all fish die, as occasionally happens with severe or acute infections, the tank must be sterilized with chlorine (see page 17) for several days, the tank should then be drained and filled with new sea water. Any residual chlorine must be neutralized with sodium thiosulfate.

Cleansing treatment may eradicate the carrier state and prevent tuberculosis from suddenly becoming symptomatic in a fish weeks or months later. This is accomplished by adding isoniazid to the tank water at the rate of 40 mg/gal, and concomitantly by feeding medicated food once a week for several months.

Tuberculosis

A. If fish is still eating:
   1. Treat in established tank along with the other fish.
   2. Remove activated carbon filter, recharge, but do not restart.
   3. Add full dose of isoniazid to the tank, 40 mg/gal.

4. Medicate food with rifampin at the rate of 6 mg/100 g of food or cycloserine at the rate of 3 mg/100 g of food and feed fish once a day in the A.M. for two weeks, then once a week for one month.

B. If fish is not eating:
   1. Remove sick fish to a small established tank (with under-gravel filtration) or to a hospital tank. Do not use activated carbon filter.
   2. Add full dose of isoniazid to the water, 40 mg/gal.
   3. Add cycloserine to the water, 50 mg/gal.
   4. Attempt to feed food medicated with rifampin, 6 mg/100 g.
   5. When eating well, fish can be returned to original tank. Continue feeding medicated food daily for two more weeks, then once a week for one month.

BACTERIAL DISEASES

All bacteria are generally divided into two large categories on the basis of their reaction to Gram's stain. Bacteria will either retain the stain and appear dark blue (Gram positive) or they will have no affinity for the stain and appear red due to the safrinine counterstain. The importance of this characterization lies in the selection of antibiotics for therapy, since these antibiotics generally are classified according to whether they are effective against most Gram positive, most Gram negative, or both categories of bacteria (Chart 1).

The vast majority of bacterial diseases of exotic marine fish that will be encountered in aquaria are "Gram negative".

It is evident that those drugs indicated for Gram positive bacteria will not usually be of value in the treatment of marine fish disease and certainly should not be used indiscriminately. They should only be used when they are demonstrated to be effective by culture and sensitivity studies.

The development of resistant strains is a serious problem in the treatment of bacterial disease, and it is imperative that when an antibiotic is selected that it be given in full dosage. A small, sublethal dose will promote the development of resistant strains, and no matter how much of the antibiotic is then used, the bacteria will multiply and kill the fish. If the fish appear to improve in the first three days with an antibiotic and then relapse, the development of resistant strains is probable and another antibiotic should be used. If the fish show no significant response in the first two days, another antibiotic should be selected. If any fish die and can be removed immediately, or if a moribund fish can be taken, then cultures and sensitivity studies may be made. However, a fish that has been dead for more than a few minutes will give unreliable information because of the rapid growth of numerous other bacteria that are always present in the tank. Marine Agar (Difco)[5] has proven to be a suitable medium for the growth of most of the pathogenic bacteria.

The principal Gram negative bacteria infecting fish belong to the genera *Pseudomonas, Aeromonas* and *Vibrio*. The signs and symptoms they cause are highly variable, depending on their virulence, water temperature, host resistance, and strain of bacteria. Usually all fish in the tank are affected to some degree and will show rapid breathing, and the water will be cloudy from the bacterial "bloom".

If a fish is breathing normally, and has no obvious skin lesion such as an ulcer or white patch, then it probably does not have a bacterial infection. Frequently all the fish in the tank will show signs of infection, but occasionally the infection will have low virulence and affect only one or two fish. The most valuable signs, in addition to rapid breathing, are clouded eyes, not tiny discrete spots but a gray to white film (Plate 7); disintegrating fins that may be reduced to a stump or have bare rays projecting, (Plate 8) or epithelium hanging loose, and reddened areas at the base of the fins.

An obvious ulcer on the side along the lateral line system or elsewhere with soft gray or red margins that daily enlarges (Plate 9), or a cloudy appearance of the fins that appear thickened, opaque, and may have blotchy white areas (Plate 7) are other signs. The fish may be hyperactive and show occasional scratch-

5. Difco Laboratories, Detroit, Michigan, U.S.A.

33

CHART 1

ANTIBIOTIC		BACTERIA			DRUG PROPERTIES		
Trade Name.	Generic Name.	Gram Pos.	Gram Neg.	Pseudomonas	Shelf Life	Solubility	Conc. for sensitivity disc in ug
Achromycin	Tetracycline hydrochloride	+	±	−	2 days	++++	30
Aerosporin	Polymyxin B	−	+	−	2 weeks plus	++++	300 units
Albamycin	Novobiocin	+	±	−	1 day	++++	30
Ampicillin	Ampicillin trihydrate	+	±	−	1-2 weeks	+++	?
Aureomycin	Chlortetracycline	+	±	−	hours only	+	30
Bacitracin	Bacitracin	+	−	−	1 week	++++	10 units
Chloromycetin	Chloramphenicol sod. succinate [2]	+	+	−	1 month	++++	30
Colymycin	Colistin sulfate	+	+	+	1 week	++++	10
Erythrocin	Erythromycin gluceptate [1]	+	±	−	1 week	+++	15
Erythrocin	Erythromycin lactobionate	+	±	−	2 weeks	+++	15
Furadantin	Nitrofurantoin sodium	+	+	−	1 day	+++	300
Gantrisin	Sulfasoxazole diolamine	+	+	−	?	++++	300
Garamycin	Gentamicin sulfate	+	+	+	3 years	++++	?
Geopen	Carbenicillin disodium	+	+	+	1 day	++++	1
Humatin	Paramomycin sulfate	−	+	+	?	++++	?

Brand	Generic					2 days plus			
Kantrex	Kanamycin	±	+	−	−	2 days plus	−	++++	30
Lincocin	Lincomycin	+	−	±	−	2 years	−	++++	2
Loridine	Cephaloridine	+	+	+	−	5 days	−	+++	?
Neobiotic	Neomycin sulfate	+	+	+	+	2 years	+	++++	30
Oleandomycin	Oleandomycin phosphate	+	−	−	−	2 weeks	−	+++	15
Penicillin G	Penicillin G	±	±	±	−	7 days	−	++++	10 units
Polycillin	Ampicillin sodium	+	+	+	−	hours only	−	++++	10
Staphcillin	Methacillin sodium	+	−	+	−	4 days	−	++++	1
Strycin	Streptomycin sulfate	±	+	+	+	1 week	+	++++	10
Sulfadiazine	Sulfadiazine sodium[3]	±	±	+	−	1 day	−	++++	300
Tegopen	Cloxacillin sodium	+	±	±	−	1 day	−	+++++	1
Terramycin	Oxytetracycline	+	+	+	−	hours only	−	++++	30
Vancocin	Vancomycin hydrochloride	+	−	±	−	2 weeks	−	++++	30
Vibramycin	Doxycycline hyclate	+	+	±	−	2 weeks	−	+	?

1) Erythromycin ethyl succinate, ethyl carbonate ester, stearate and estolate are insoluble in water. Erythromycin is slightly soluble.

2) Chloramphenicol is slightly soluble in water. Chloramphenicol palmitate is insoluble.

3) Sodium sulfadiazine is precipitated in water with pH below 9.

ing behavior, or they may be listless resting on the bottom or at the surface panting. If suffering from an internal bacterial disease, diagnosis may be extremely difficult. The liver or kidneys are usually affected, and they will not eat. They will be listless, and while the fins may become frayed, they usually do not scratch or show skin lesions.

A bacterial infection must be differentiated from a high ammonia or nitrite level in the water, because the toxic effects of these chemicals will similarly give rapid breathing, listlessness, fraying of fins, and loss of appetite. All the fish in the tank will be affected, some to a greater or lesser degree in the case of ammonia or nitrite toxicity, but they will not have skin lesions or cloudy eyes. The most reliable differentiation between this and bacterial disease is to test the water for elevated levels of nitrite or ammonia.

Occasionally the organism is so virulent that rapid breathing g and listlessness are the only signs and death ensues within 24 hours or less, before other signs can develop. Sometimes the bacteria produce a potent toxin and death is even more rapid, in six to twelve hours, but again all the fish in the tank will be affected. If the organism is of relatively low virulence, only one fish may be infected, as evidenced by the formation of one or several ulcers, and there may be normal breathing and eating at first. This type of infection is usually consequent to traumatic injury of the skin or fins. Such damage may be inflicted during capture or nipping by other fish. (Plates 10, 11).

Myxobacteria[6] of the genus *Chondrococcus* cause occasional infections in marine fish that are usually confined to one fish and produce lesions similar to columnaris disease of fresh water fish. The lesions are white or gray and resemble a small tuft of cotton. It may be difficult to distinguish between this and *Saprolegnia* fungus infection by external appearance. Frequently the initial lesions are grayish-white at the outer margins of the fins with strings and flakes of tissue hanging in the water. Microscopically *Myxobacteria* are easily differentiated by the Gram stain since all fungi are Gram positive and the *Myxobacteria* are Gram negative. The bacilli form long thin rods which are slowly motile in wet slide preparations.

6. Bullock, G. L., Conroy, D. A., Snieszko, S. K.: Bacterial Diseases of Fishes, Pub. T. F. H., 1971.

Treatment:

While ultraviolet light, ozone, low chlorine levels and other such measures may be helpful in limiting bacterial growth or the transmission from one fish to another, they are of no real value in the treatment of an established bacterial infection in a fish. Prompt and aggressive treatment with antibiotics is required when many fish appear sick, and because the bacteria are present throughout the tank, the fish should not be removed for treatment.

If one or two fish are suffering from ulceration of the tail, fins or body, they may be removed to a one to five gallon hospital tank for treatment to conserve medication. The problem is to select an antibiotic that the bacteria is sensitive to before the fish die. Numerous experiments have demonstrated that chloramphenicol (Chloromycetin), gentamycin (Garamycin) and neomycin are effective in most cases. Kanamycin, colistin, polymyxin-B, and sulfasoxazole are frequently successful. Occasionally the bacteria will be resistant to these drugs and erythromycin, or with less confidence, tetracycline can be tried. If these fail, only culture and isolation of the organism with the establishment of antibiotic sensitivities will resolve the problem. Antibiotics that are generally not satisfactory are penicillin, nitrofurantoin, ampicillin, tetracycline, streptomycin, and sulfa drugs. Nifurpirinol (Furanace, Abbott) may be useful in fresh water systems, but has not shown outstanding results so far in salt water aquaria.

Bacterial Diseases

A. If infection is serious with many fish affected:
1. Remove all fish and invertebrates to hospital tank with air stone.
2. Add neomycin, 250 mg/gal., and chloramphenicol sodium succinate, 50 mg/gal. to hospital tank. Do not feed.
3. Alternatively add gentamycin sulfate 20 mg/gal.
4. Sterilize original tank with chlorine (See page 17) for 24 hours. Then neutralize the chlorine with sodium thiosulfate. Check for complete neutralization with chlorine indicator reagent

and smell.

5. If antibiotics are effective, treatment should take 3-5 days.

B. If mild infection with only one or two fish showing fin-tail rot or ulcer:
1. Remove affected fish and treat as above in hospital tank with air stone.
2. If ulcer has dead flesh surrounding it, dab ulcer with merthiolate, rinse fish in sea water and return to hospital tank.
3. Return fish to original tank when redness disappears from around ulcer or from margin of tail rot. Treatment is usually complete in 3-5 days.

EXTERNAL FUNGUS (SAPROLEGNIA)

The diagnosis of this disease depends upon seeing the lesion which is cottony or wooly in appearance and white or gray in color (Plate 12). It may be located anywhere on the body, but usually starts as a complication of an ulcer as a secondary invader. Untreated it will gradually enlarge over a period of many days or several weeks. Eventually the mycelia invade and destroy internal structures and spread to various organs in the body resulting in the death of the fish.

Treatment:

Early infection with *Saprolegnia* may resolve with antibiotic treatment of the underlying ulcer. A serious case is frequently resistant to all treatment, and effective medications for this purpose are not generally available. Therapy that has been reported to be successful consists of painting the lesion with merthiolate or a 1:10 solution of iodine. The fish is held out of the water in the hand for application of the antiseptic, then is rinsed in a small amount of sea water and then placed in a hospital tank containing potassium dichromate 1.0 gram/6 gal.

As soon as the lesion has cleared, the fish is returned to an established tank. Phenoxethol (2-phenoxyethanol) is reported to be effective. The recommended dosage is 38 to 75 ml/gal. of a 1% solution. This should be added to the tank and food should be soaked in this prior to feeding.[7] Furanace (Nifurpirinol, Abbott) is claimed to be effective against *Saprolegnia*, but caution should be used because of the possibility of destroying the beneficial bacteria in the biologic under-gravel filter. Its use should be limited to the hospital tank.

In the author's experience, superficial treatments such as iodine, merthiolate, malachite green, potassium permanganate, and potassium dichromate swabs and baths are only temporarily effective. Systemic treatment by medication administered in food is usually required. Considerable research is needed in this area to develop effective antifungal agents.

External Fungus

1. Remove affected fish to hospital tank with air stone.
2. Add 50 cc/gal. of a 1% solution of phenoxethol.
3. Soak food in the same medication, or add by medicine dropper to food prior to feeding.
4. If there is an underlying ulcer or other lesion, treat by adding 250 mg of neomycin plus 50 mg of chloramphenicol sodium succinate to each gallon of water. Treat for 5-7 days.

LYMPHOCYSTIS

Only one or two, but occasionally many fish in a tank will show this infection at one time. The lesion is unique and is gray, papillomatous and very sharply demarcated. It is usually seen on a fin, but may be anywhere on the body. Occasionally the growths are scattered over the entire body and fins. When located about the mouth (Plate 13) it may interfere with feeding and the fish may die, but in most other instances the disease disappears and does not kill the fish which cures itself spontaneously.

7. Reichenbach-klinke, H. and Elkan, E. The Principal Diseases of Lower Vertebrates: Diseases of Fishes. Academic Press (London). 1965. p 135.

INTESTINAL TREMATODES

The diagnosis of this condition is difficult. It appears to cause no symptoms in most fish, but if the trematodes are extremely numerous, the fish may stop eating, show poor or light coloration, develop a sunken abdomen, become malnourished and die. Occasionally the trematodes may perforate the gut wall and cause peritonitis in which case the fish dies suddenly. They may also infiltrate the bile ducts of the liver resulting in debilitation and failure to eat. Since a high percentage of wild fish have intestinal trematodes, it can be assumed that a fish that is not apparently sick, does not elicit rapid breathing, with no skin or fin lesions, that possibly swims with dorsal fin clamped down and is a picky eater, has intestinal trematodes. At least a trial treatment is in order. If the fish does not improve, then a more serious internal disease may exist, such as *Coccidiosis* or *Ichthyophonus*.

Treatment:

Piperazine, a relatively non-toxic drug, should be given in the food once a day at the rate of 250 mg/100 gm of moist food, for a period of 10 days.

GILL PARASITES

When there is rapid breathing and no other signs of sickness and only one or two fish in a community tank are affected, it indicates one of two diseases: bacterial infection or gill parasites (excluding *Oodinium* and *Cryptocaryon*). If the fish is eating and acting normally but occasionally scratches the opercula, then the diagnosis is relatively certain. The usual infecting parasites are gill flukes or trematodes, and *Trichodina*. Usually there is no progression of the disease over a period of days or weeks. If the fish is not eating, breathing rapidly, and there is progressive deterioration of health, then other conditions should be considered first, such as *Oodinium*, *Cryptocaryon* or bacterial infection (especially tuberculosis).

Treatment:

A bath is prepared using one gallon of sea water to which is added 1 cc of formaldehyde. The water is aerated with an air stone, and the fish is placed in the bath for 15 minutes. If the fish shows no signs of distress, it can be left for a total of 30 minutes and is then transferred to a hospital tank containing quinacrine hydrochloride. It may be necessary to repeat the formalin bath treatment in several days if symptoms persist before returning the fish to its original tank. Formaldehyde should not be added to the established tank because it will destroy the beneficial bacteria in the biologic filter if present in sufficient concentration to kill any parasites or bacteria, and it is very slowly degraded.

Caution should be used in the selection of formaldehyde for the preparation of the bath because methyl alcohol is usually used as a stabilizer and is highly toxic to fish. Use formaldehyde with the least amount of methyl alcohol obtainable. Add 1 cc for each gallon of sea water and aerate vigorously for 24 hours to remove most of the alcohol before adding any fish. *Trichodina* are best treated with quinacrine hydrochloride as for *Cryptocaryon irritans*.

Gill Parasites

1. Prepare bath by adding 1 cc of formaldehyde to one gallon of sea water. Aerate vigorously for 24 hours.
2. Remove affected fish to bath for 15 - 30 minutes.
3. Transfer to hospital tank with air stone. Add quinacrine hydrochloride 8-12 mg/gal. of water in divided doses, ½ now and ½ in 6-12 hours.
4. Feed flake food once a day sparingly.
5. Repeat step #1 on third day and return fish to original tank.

HIGH AMMONIA OR NITRITE LEVEL

The principal waste product of metabolism in fish is ammonia, excreted through the gills and in the urine. The only way this can be converted to nitrite and then to less toxic nitrate is by bacteria (*Nitrobacter* and *Nitrosomonas*, or similar marine types). Therefore, in shipping bags, hospital tank and tanks or vessels that have no biologic filter established, there will be no nitrite or nitrate and ammonia will be the toxic agent that builds up and limits the time the fish may be kept in that water. Very small amounts of ammonia begin to have a toxic effect

(0.01 ppm un-ionized form) whereas a greater amount of nitrite is tolerated (up to 0.1 ppm)[9]. Some fish can tolerate much higher levels of both products. Toxic effects are noted primarily in the gills where the filaments become hyperplastic and thickened to the degree that respiration is less efficient. The fish will begin to show rapid breathing, and all the fish in a community tank will be affected, although to varying degrees of severity. Eventually they will stop eating and the fins will become frayed or ragged. There is slow progression of effects and the fish become more susceptible to infection by bacteria, fungi, or protozoa. If they carry quiescent internal parasites, these may then flourish and kill the fish.

High Ammonia or Nitrite

1. If the tank has no biologic filter, change the water.
2. If the tank has a biologic filter, measure the nitrite level. A slight trace is acceptable, but if the nitrite nitrogen measures higher than 0.1 ppm by test kit, then remedial steps must be taken to lower it. Check the following points:
A. If the biologic (under-gravel) filter has not been in operation for three weeks, allow this period of time for the build-up of nitrifying bacteria.
B. The tank has more live specimens than recommended (3 inches of animal per square foot of filter bed surface area). If this is the case, remove some specimens and recheck the nitrite level in several days.
C. The under-gravel filter is not functioning at maximum capacity; the gravel size is too large to provide enough surface area for bacteria; the gravel is less than 2 inches in depth (2 to 3 inches is optimum); bacterial growth has been inhibited by chemicals contaminating the tank (formalin, antibiotics, chlorine, organic chemical fumes, or insecticides). In this case begin activated carbon filtration or replenish the carbon filter. It should

9. Spotte, S. Marine Aquarium Keeping. Pub. John Wiley & Sons, Inc., 1973, pp 50 - 56.

be noted that such antibiotics as chloramphenicol (Chloromycetin) and gentamycin (Garamycin) do not appear to completely destroy the biologic filter and it may recover, probably with the development of resistant strains that will be much less sensitive if later such antibiotics are added again to the tank.

ICHTHYOPHONUS

This is such a common disease that nearly all fish seem to carry it. Progression is usually very slow and symptoms will depend upon which internal organs are most affected. The diagnosis is secure if the fish manifests vertigo, listlessness, and exophthalmos (popeye) (Plate 14). This indicates severe infection of the brain and optic tracts or area behind the eyes. The mouth is usually open and rigid, so that the fish is never seen to close it. Rapid breathing results from infection of the gills or possibly liver or heart failure from infection of those organs. Occasionally the skin will have small rough elevations (Plate 15). When the intestinal tract, pancreas, or liver are principally affected, the fish, may stop eating and develop a sunken or pinched appearance of the abdomen. Malnutrition results in frayed or ragged fins and poor coloration. With such a complex of symptoms, the disease may mimic many other diseases and a definitive diagnosis may be impossible. The most important signs and symptoms are: only one fish in a community tank is affected with vertigo or loss of balance, and listlessness. Bacterial infections that cause some problems with equilibrium will generally affect many fish in a community tank and there may be additional signs such as cloudy eyes, skin lesions and rapid breathing amongst all those affected. Exophthalmos and listlessness may be seen in tuberculosis, but the fish generally does not have vertigo, usually it has raised scales, blotchy coloration, ragged fins, and it always has rapid breathing. In the absence of vertigo, the diagnosis must usually be made by elimination. The course of the disease and progression of symptoms is slow, and the fish may survive for weeks with the above symptoms.

Treatment:

An adequate cure for this condition has not been found,

although 2-phenoxyethanol has been recommended in the dosage of 38 to 75 cc of a 1% solution/gal. plus feeding with dry food soaked in medication.[10] The author has not been able to cure the disease with this medication. At present, preventive care is the only way to keep this disease in check, and this involves maintaining water quality, good nutrition, avoidance of overcrowding, and good tank hygiene.

10. Van Duijn, C.: Diseases of Fishes, pub. Iliffe Books Ltd., London, 1967, p. 291.

5. PATHOLOGY AND LABORATORY IDENTIFICATION

This section is for the scientist, researcher and aquarist who wishes to probe deeper into the nature of the disease organisms. It details their life cycles, microscopic appearance and methods of identification by the use of relatively simple laboratory techniques. Certainly anyone whose livelihood depends upon marketing healthy fish should obtain an inexpensive microscope (with color corrected achromatic lenses) and learn to screen his fish for most of the common diseases using the methods detailed in this section.

OODINIUM OCELLATUM

Oodinium is a dinoflagellate belonging to the same order as *Gymnodinium breve* which is a highly toxic dinoflagellate and causes the red tide in Florida waters. The life cycle is simple,

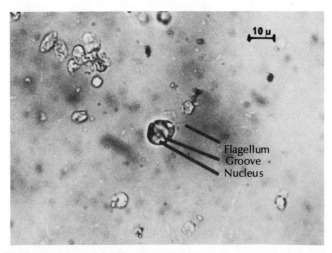

Fig. 1. Dinospore of *Oodinium ocellatum*, wet mount of skin scraping from Navarchus Angel. Note the circumferential groove and terminal flagellum. A large pale nucleus occupies much of the cell. The tumbling motion when swimming is characteristic.

beginning with the free swimming and infective form (dino-spore Fig. 1), that has one flagellum for swimming and another that encircles the body in a constricted waistline groove.

The dinospore is very small, measuring 9-15 microns, and moves very rapidly across the field when seen microscopically. It is said that this stage will die within 24 hours if a host is not found to infect[11]. However, the author has found one strain to survive and remain infective for at least four weeks. Once the organism has become attached to the gill epithelium or the skin, it becomes rounded (Fig. 2, Plate 16) and develops a small funnel-shaped aperture at one end (Plate 17) through which project rhizoids or root-like filaments that invade the host cells to obtain nutrition. The organism grows and much of the internal structure becomes obscured by globular starch granules.

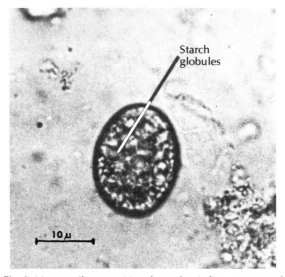

Fig. 2. Non-motile stage. Note loss of waistline groove and of flagella. Cytoplasm contains many starch globules obscuring the internal structure. Wet mount of skin scraping.

Various figures are given for the size of this stage, but 15-150 microns seems to cover the range.[11] A round or oval macronucleus is present and the cyptoplasm is filled with fine spheroidal bodies or droplets. The cell wall or membrane is sharp and clearly visible, and is said to contain chitin. The organism damages the gill epithelium causing hemorrhages and adhesions of

11. Reichenbach-klinke, H. Fish Pathology. 1973. Pub. T. F. H., p. 153.

filaments. It is said to cause death by interference with respiration, but many fish autopsied by the author have had relatively few organisms in the gills and the question of toxin production is raised. The gills appear to be infected primarily and the fish may die before the characteristic white powdery or dust-like appearance of the organisms on the skin is observed. The cyst stage is formed when the rhizoids retract and the opening is sealed with a cellulose cap (Fig. 3).

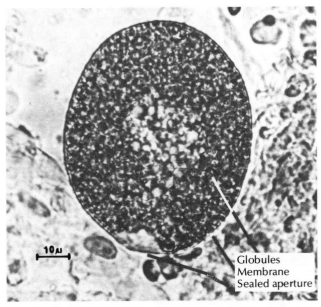

Fig. 3. Cyst stage of *Oodinium* from Mangrove Snapper. Wet preparation from gill. The organism appears dark because of numerous cytoplasmic globules. Note distinct limiting membrane and sealed aperture at the lower end through which the rhizoids projected in the previous stage of attachment.

It is during the cyst stage that internal divisions take place. Such dividing cells are termed the palmella stage and divisions progress from 2 (Plate 18) to 4 to 8 to 16 and so on to 256.

While the cyst stage generally falls to the bottom of the tank, it may remain entrapped in the gill filaments as seen in Fig. 3. The rate of development of the daughter cells in the cyst is greatly dependent on temperature with no divisions occurring at temperatures below 50°F (10°C), slow rate of division at 68-77°F (20-25°C) and optimal rate at temperatures above 77°F

47

(25°C) when the dinospores are formed and released in three days. They rapidly disperse by means of flagella to reinfect the fish which, in the author's experience, show signs of infection on the 6th to 7th day at 77°F (25°C).

Demonstration of the Organism:
Equipment:
1. Microscope (simple type but with color corrected or achromatic lenses and capable of 150 X magnification.)
2. Metal spatula.
3. Glass microscope slides.
4. Glass coverslips.

Method:
The infected fish is netted or caught in a transparent plastic cup or bag, picked up gently but securely in the left hand, and then holding the spatula in the right hand, the tail, sides or any fin conveniently exposed is firmly scraped onto the glass slide. This material should include several scales along with mucous (slime), epithelium, and the organisms. A drop of tank water is added, stirred, and a glass coverslip placed on top and gently pressed to exclude any bubbles. The bottom of the slide is wiped dry and it is ready for microscopic examination. The microscope mirror is adjusted for intense even illumination and the slide is examined using the lowest magnification first.

What to look for:
1. The earliest stage, the dinospore (Fig. 1), may be present with later stages and appears as a small ball at 150 X magnification that moves rapidly across the field in a wavy 'bee-line' with pronounced tumbling motion; then suddenly changes direction and swims off at an angle. The organism measures about 10 μ and will be smaller than cells from the skin and a very small fraction the size of a scale. The long flagella may not be visible, but the waist or midline constriction of the body and the general ball shape is discernable at this magnification. Several such organisms should be present in the microscopic field if this stage is present at all.
2. The vegetative form (Fig. 2) is much larger measuring about 60 μ in length, slightly oblong in shape, dark colored and non-motile. This is the stage that resides firmly attached to skin or gills by rhizoids (rootlet processes for nutrition) that project from a small aperture at one end (Plate 17). The

rhizoids cannot be seen at 100 X magnification. The organism at this stage is distinguished from *Cryptocaryon* by the absence of cilia, absence of movement, and the presence of numerous large starch granules that obscure the nucleus and a few greenish tinted granules (chromatophores) in the cytoplasm. The starch granules may be further demonstrated by the addition of a drop of iodine to the edge of the coverslip which diffuses beneath and stains the granules purplishblack. If a fish is moribund or has recently died, the gill filaments may be removed and prepared in the same way as the skin scraping. An effort should be made to get a single layer of filament, excluding any bulky pieces that would elevate the coverslip. A razor blade or two needles may be useful for this purpose. The vegetative organisms will be seen between lamellae of the filament as dark, oblong non-motile cells. (Fig. 2).

CRYPTOCARYON IRRITANS

This ciliated protozoan parasite of marine fishes is closely related to fresh water "Ich" (*Ichthyophthirius multifilis*) and carries the trivial name "White Spot disease". It was later described under the name of *Ichthyophthirius marinus*, but the first description and name given by Brown in 1951[12] prevails.

Infection with this organism is very frequent in marine aquaria and whenever a wild fish that has not had a cleansing treatment is added to an established community tank, one can expect an outbreak of this disease. This outbreak, if left untreated, will usually kill all the fish in a small closed system. In a large commercial closed system with extensive filtration or in an open system, the course of the disease is slower, may remain quiescent, or may occasionally die out.

The first stage in the life cycle is the rapidly motile, infective form, the tomite (Fig. 4) that is newly released from the cyst by the hundreds and measures about 55 x 35 microns. After a short time, probably less than 24 hours, they attack the host fish and develop a conspicuous buccal cavity and feeding apparatus (Fig. 5). Cilia cover the flask-shaped body and are long and active. This stage is called the trophont. A meganucleus is visible and composed of up to four spherical bodies. The remainder of the

12. Brown, E. M.: A New Parasitic Protozoan The Casual Organism of a White Spot Disease in Marine Fish - Cryptocaryon irritans (Gen. & Spec. N.) Agenda Sci. Meetings, Zool. Soc. London, 1950, No. 11: 1-2.

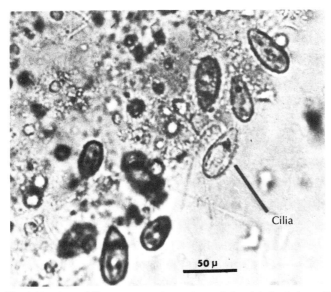

Fig. 4. Tomites of *Cryptocaryon* devouring cellular debris. At least 10 can be seen. Wet preparation of filter concentrated water occupied by French Angel (Plate 4). Note the pear-shape and faint long cilia.

cytoplasm is filled with small spherical bodies, some vacuolated, and some with food material ingested by the parasite. As the organism feeds on the epidermis or gills of the fish, it gradually enlarges. The mouth becomes relatively less conspicuous and the cilia shorter (Fig. 6). The feeding trophonts are quite destructive, causing erosions and finally fine pin-point ulcers of the skin, and loss of gill epithelium. They may invade the branching vessels of gills and interfere with blood circulation (Plate 19). They may burrow beneath the skin and when occupying such deep location, they are particularly difficult to eradicate with treatment. Finally, the trophont ceases to feed, becomes spherical, and begins to encyst. This stage prior to encystment is called the tomont. It either drops off or remains on the fish and is seen to be filled with hundreds or thousands of globoid bodies that obscure the nucleus.

The cysts (Fig. 7) vary considerably in size, depending upon how well fed the trophonts were and what size they grew to prior to encystment. Various investigators have found them to range from 170 to 450 microns. Nigrelli, et al,[13] found the tomites emerged from the cysts in six to nine days with most of them emerging on the eighth day under test tube conditions. This is similar to the author's experience with infected fish at a water temperature of 82°F (27.8°C). Colder temperatures may have a considerable retarding effect on this period.

Demonstration of the Organism:

Equipment:

1. Microscope (simple type but with color corrected or achromatic lenses and capable of 100 X magnification).
2. Metal spatula.
3. Glass microscope slides.
4. Glass coverslips.

Method:

The infected fish is netted or caught in a transparent plastic cup or bag, picked up gently but securely in the left hand, and then holding the spatula in the right hand, the tail, sides or any fin conveniently exposed is firmly scraped onto the glass slide. This material should include several scales along with mucous (slime), epithelium, and the organisms. A drop of tank water is added, stirred, and a glass coverslip placed on top and gently pressed to exclude any air bubbles. The bottom of the slide is wiped dry and it is ready for microscopic examination. The microscope mirror is adjusted for intense, even illumination and the slide is examined using the lowest magnification first.

What to look for:

1. The earliest stage, if present, will consist of several to many pyriform (pear-shaped) ciliated organisms measuring about 35 x 55μ. The tomites (Fig. 4) resemble ants at a bread crumb, nibbling, backing up, advancing and surrounding the epithelium. They continuously move in short spurts.
2. As they grow, the cytoplasm of the tomites acquires more granules and they lose their pyriform shape becoming flask-shaped with a somewhat flexible feeding end, the trophont (Fig. 5). Again, they will work back and forth around cellular debris.
3. When the infection has been present many days, the

13. Nigrelli, R. F., and Ruggieri, G. D.: Enzcotics in the New York Aquarium Caused by Cryptocaryon irritans Brown, 1956 (h Ichthyophthirius marinus Sikama, 1961), a Histophagus Ciliate in the Skin, Eyes and Gills of Marine Fishes. Zoologica, 51, No. 3, pp. 97-102.

trophonts will become much larger, possibly up to ⅛ the size of a scale (170-450μ) and will usually be seen on or close to a scale. They move in a slow smooth fashion but the cilia are now very short and may be difficult to see at 100 X magnification (Fig. 6).

4. The cyst or tomont stage measures up to 450μ, is non-motile and has a thickened cell wall (Fig. 7).

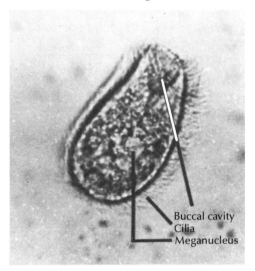

Fig. 5. Trophont of *Cryptocaryon*. Wet preparation from fin scraping of Four-eye Butterfly. The cilia and buccal cavity are plainly seen. A protrusible feeding apparatus is retracted. Connected spherical bodies forming a portion of the meganucleus are visible centrally.

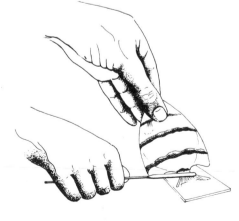

Preparation of a wet smear by scraping slime and scales onto a glass slide.

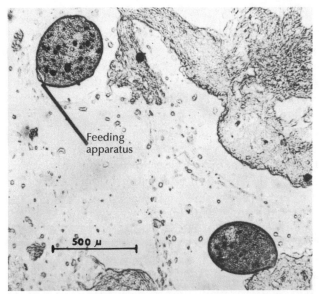

Fig. 6. Two mature trophonts of *Cryptocaryon*. Wet preparation from fin scraping of Tomato Clown. Cilia are short and inconspicuous at this stage and movement is slow. The buccal area with protruded feeding apparatus is visible at one end.

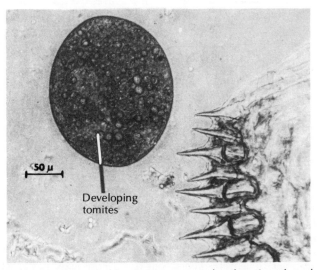

Fig. 7. Cyst or tomont of *Cryptocaryon* next to basal portion of a scale. From Teardrop Butterfly of Plate 2. The cell is filled with developing tomites, immobile and devoid of cilia or feeding apparatus.

TUBERCULOSIS

Fish tuberculosis is caused by bacteria belonging to the genus *Mycobacteria*. Bacilli of the same genus are responsible for human tuberculosis, however, in fish the organism is *M. marinum*. An additional species may be found in fresh water fish (*M. fortuitum*). The disease is world wide in distribution and the natural mode of transmission is said to be from oral ingestion of the bacteria.[14]

As in humans, tuberculosis produces a chronic debilitating disease. Symptoms slowly progress over a period of several months. There is loss of appetite and secretive behavior. One of the first tangible signs is rapid breathing which is very shallow. An important differential point is that the other fish in the tank are not breathing in this manner. Gradually other signs develop as a result of poor nutrition and disease of internal organs: ragged fins, faded colors, blotchy pale areas on the skin, and raised scales giving the fish a "moth-eaten" appearance (Plate 5). The abdomen becomes sunken. Internally, granulomas are formed in several or many organs, particularly the liver, spleen, and kidneys, but also frequently in peritoneum, gut wall, gills (Fig. 27) and behind the eyes. This retro-orbital lesion is responsible for the appearance of exophthalmos (Plate 6).

Microscopically, the granulomas are irregular or round with outer laminated connective tissue layers and central necrosis(Plate 21 & 22). Occasional histiocytes are present, but multinucleated giant cells are not usually produced in fish. Bacilli can usually be demonstrated in the granulomas by the acid fast stain, see page 55 (Ziehl-Neelsen) (Plate 23 & 24). The organism grows well in culture on special nutritive media, mentioned on page 56.

Colonies of 2-3 mm size are observed on the media in two weeks at room temperature. They are lemon yellow, elevated, smooth, and moist (Plate 25).

Demonstration of the Organism:
Equipment:
1. Microscope with achromatic lenses and capable of 400 X magnification.

14. Nigrelli, R. F., Vogel, H.: Spontaneous Tuberculosis in Fishes and in Other Cold Blooded Vertebrates with Special Reference to Mycobacterium fortuitum Cruz from Fish and Human Lesions. Zoologica 48, No. 9, 1963, pp. 130-143.

2. Microscope slides.

3. Spatula

4. Culture plates or slants.

5. Stain for acid-fast bacteria. The Ziehl-Neelsen method is suitable using carbol fuchsin - methylene blue stain.
   It is prepared as follows:
   Basic fuchsin (90% dye content) .... 0.3 gm.
   Alcohol (95%) .... 10 ml.
   Prepare separately:
   Methylene blue (90% dye content) .... 0.3 gm.
   Alcohol (95%) .... 30 ml.
   dissolve and add to 100 ml of dilute potassium hydroxide (KOH 0.01% by weight).

Method:

Prepare thin smears on microscopic slides by scraping gill filaments, skin ulcers, eroded fins, or other diseased areas and squashing the debris onto the slide, or by squashing bits of necrotic or nodular areas of liver or spleen. The material can be squashed with a coverslip which is then slid off and the smear air dried and stained as follows:

1. Place the slide on a cork in a dish and flood with carbol fuchsin stain. Lift the slide with forceps and apply heat to the undersurface with a cigarette lighter, alcohol lamp or small bunsen burner until the surface of the stain begins to steam. Continue the warmth for three to five minutes, adding more stain as necessary to prevent drying.

2. Rinse in running tap water.

3. Flood briefly with the 95% alcohol solution containing 3% hydrochloric acid (by volume) until most of the red stain has washed out leaving only a faint suggestion of pink color.

4. Wash in tap water.

5. Counterstain by flooding the slide with methylene blue stain for 30 seconds.

6. Wash in water.

7. Dry and examine with the microscope using a magnification of 400 X.

What to look for:

Mycobacteria, in contrast to other bacteria, hold the red stain and are not decolorized by the acid-alcohol solution unless it is applied too long. The acid fast bacteria appear as bright red, thin, beaded rods that are very small (about 0.5 x 3u) (Plate 24). They may be distributed singly or lie in packets like a clump of straw.

Another method of identification is to grow the *Mycobacteria* on nutrient selective media where the colonies can be recognized by their characteristic appearance. For this purpose use Middlebrook 7H10 or Lowenstein-Jensen media (Difco Labs, Detroit, Mich.). The infected material is streaked across the surface of the agar and the plates or slants are left at room temperature with some daylight available. Typical colonies will appear in 2 - 3 weeks and will be lemon yellow, elevated, smooth and moist (Plate 25). Microscopic slide smears may be prepared from the colonies and stained by the Ziehl-Neelsen method.

BACTERIAL DISEASES

The agents of bacterial diseases of exotic marine fish are all Gram negative bacilli (except for *Mycobacteria*, considered separately).

Vibrio Disease — caused by *Vibrio anguillarium* and *Vibrio parahemolyticus*. They produce hemorrhagic septicemia (infection carried by the blood stream), characterized by hemorrhagic lesions on the body or base of caudal peduncle, boils of the skin which may ulcerate with hemorrhagic margins (Plate 9 & 26), thickening of the epithelium of fins, exophthalmos (rarely), and necrosis of kidneys (Plate 27). The bacillus is a polar flagellated, motile, curved thick rod that is capable of carbohydrate fermentation. Growth is aerobic on Furunculosis Agar (Difco Labs, Detroit, Mich.), Marine Agar (Difco), or Trypticase Soy Agar (Baltimore Biological Labs, Baltimore, Md.) containing 1.5% sea salts.

Pseudomonas - Aeromonas Diseases — caused by *Pseudomonas fluorescens*, *Pseudomonas* sp , and *Aeromonas liquefaciens*. One manifestation of infection consists of ulcers that are deep, extending to muscle, and have white necrotic margins. Another form is infectious dermatitis with inflammation and color change of the skin. Fin, tail and body rot are also caused by these organisms.

The bacilli are Gram negative, motile with a polar flagellum, and grow well on the same media as *Vibrio*. Their differentiation and specific identification require highly specialized bacteriologic techniques.[15]

It must be emphasized that the overlap in signs and symptoms of bacterial infection by *Vibrio*, *Aeromonas* and *Pseudomonas* are so great that it is usually not possible to tell which organism is responsible for the disease in the individual case without specific bacteriologic identification, nor is it generally necessary. In case treatment with antibiotics previously known to be effective against Gram negative bacteria, particularly *Pseudomonas*, fail to effect a cure, then antibiotic sensitivity studies may be necessary.

Columnaris Disease — caused by *Chondrococcus columnaris*. These are long, thin rods measuring up to 10μ in length and less than 1μ diameter. They belong to the order of *Myxobacteria*, and the organism is probably the same as that found in fresh water fish where it is known as "cotton wool disease" or "mouth fungus". Of course, it is not fungus, and can be differentiated from fungus hyphae by its motility, lack of branching, and Gram negative staining reaction. Skin, gills and internal organs may be infected. The bacteria are aerobic and produce flat, spreading, irregular colonies that are yellow pigmented on media with reduced agar content (1%).

Demonstration of the Organism:

Equipment:

1. Microscope capable of 400 X magnification
2. Glass microscope slides and coverslips
3. Scraper or metal spatula
4. Gram's stain (See page 59)

Method:

Scrapings of the suspected bacterial lesion are spread out thinly in the center of the slide and allowed to air dry. The slide is then stained with Gram's stain by the method given on page 59.

What to look for:

Gram positive bacteria will be deep blue while Gram negative bacteria will be red (Plate 28). *Columnaris* organisms are long filamentous rods (Plate 29). *Mycobacteria* (T.B.) are Gram positive (blue) as are *Saprolegnia* fungi.

In the wet preparation, *Columnaris* filamentous rods will

15. Bullock, G. L., Conroy, D. A., and Sniezko, S F.: Bacterial Diseases of Fishes. 1971. T. F. H. Pub.

57

show slow undulating movement. This preparation will help to rule out infection with protozoa such as *Cryptocaryon*.

These examinations are of only limited usefulness. The question of infection with some pathogen other than bacteria can be settled, but if the bacteria are Gram negative (red), then one of the following conclusions pertains:

1. The bacteria are primary pathogens.
2. The bacteria are secondary invaders, possibly proteolytic, that are pathogenic for a weakened host.
3. They are heterotrophic, proteolytic bacteria invading a dying fish and may be pathogenic only in massive numbers.
4. The bacteria are normal flora that occur on the body surfaces and sometimes in tissues of the host but are not pathogenic.

If a definitive diagnosis cannot be made on the basis of the appearance of the lesions, symptoms and microscopic examination of wet and stained slides, then it will be necessary to grow the bacteria in culture and identify them by bacteriologic techniques that are beyond the scope of this manual.

Antibiotic susceptability (sensitivity) testing: The simplest method is disc diffusion on agar plate in which a Marine Agar plate (Difco) is streaked with the contaminated material using a sterile cotton swab in such a manner as to produce a uniform confluent distribution of bacteria over the surface. Small filter paper discs*, cut with a cork borer and sterilized, are dipped in different antibiotic solutions and evenly distributed over the surface of the agar plate (Plate 30). Reference numbers are placed on the outside (back) of the plate to code the antibiotic in the disc for final interpretation.

The plate is then left at room temperature for 1 - 2 days, and the bacterial susceptability compared by the size of the clear zone of inhibition where bacteria fail to grow around the disc. Generally, a wide zone indicates that the antibiotic should be effective and no zone means the bacteria are resistant to the drug. The concentration of antibiotic to be used in the discs is indicated in table 1.

*Ed. Note: These filter discs and agar plates of almost any media are available commercially from laboratory supply houses.

EXTERNAL FUNGI

External fungus infections in marine fish are rare, and are nearly always secondary invaders of an existing lesion such as traumatic ulcers or wounds inflicted by other fish. In addition, it is probable that the fish have a low level of resistance due to environmental factors or internal disease. Case reports for marine fish in the literature are scant, and it is only under aquarium conditions that this disease seems to occur with any frequency. The same genus of fungus that is so frequent in fresh water aquarium fish is responsible for the occasional case seen in marine systems: *Saprolegnia*. This is a member of the class *Phycomycetes* and is characterized by long, thin, non-septate, occasionally branching hyphae that stain blue with Gram's stain. (Plate 31). This characterization easily differentiates them microscopically from the *Myxobacteria* but the external lesion bears some similarity in its cotton-like tufted appearance. The mycelium (roots) of the fungus colony invades the soft tissues as well as the cartilage of the fish producing an ever enlarging ulcerated lesion. (Plate 32). The mycelia then infiltrate other organs including liver, gut, peritoneum and kidneys and cause extensive necrosis and eventually death of the fish.

Demonstration of the Organism:

Equipment:

1. Microscope capable of 150 X magnification.
2. Metal spatula or scraper.
3. Glass microscope slides.
4. Gram's stain.

Method:

The infected fish is caught in a transparent plastic bag or cup and held gently but firmly in the hand. The fungus lesion is scraped onto two slides. One slide is air dried while the other is cover slipped and examined as a wet preparation under the microscope. The air dried slide is stained with Gram's stain as follows:

Solutions:

A. Crystal violet (90% dye content) .... 2 gm.
   Ethyl alcohol (95%) .... 20 cc.
B. Ammonium oxalate .... 0.8 gm.
   Distilled water .... 80 cc.

Mix solutions A and B.

C. Iodine .... 1 gm.
   Potassium iodide .... 2 gm.
   Distilled water .... 300 cc.
D. Safranine 0 (2.5% solution in 95% alcohol) .... 10 cc.
   Distilled water .... 100 cc.

Procedure:
1. Flood the slides for 1 min. with crystal violet (A+B).
2. Rinse in tap water briefly.
3. Flood slide with iodine solution (C) for 1 minute.
4. Rinse in tap water.
5. Decolorize for 10 seconds with 95% ethyl alcohol.
6. Counterstain 1 minute with safranine.
7. Rinse in tap water.
8. Blot, air dry, add one drop of mounting media and coverslip.

What to look for:

The mycelia of *Saprolegnia* will appear as a matted inter-twining mass of long thread-like structures staining bluish-black with Gram's stain. (Plate 31). They are branching and non-septate(no cross partitions, Fig. 8,9).Dead hyphae may stain red.

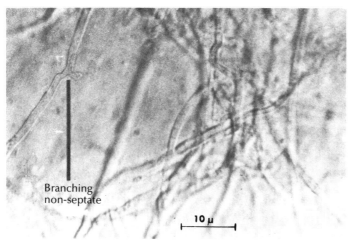

Fig. 8. *Saprolegnia*. Wet mount of scraping from mouth of Maroon Clown seen in Plate 12. Note branching of non-septate hyphae.

Myxobacteria, which look very similar both in the gross appearance of the lesion and microscopically, will be gram negative, that is, will stain red with Gram's stain. They will also be seen to move slowly in the wet preparation, and no branching of the filaments will be seen.

Saprolegnia can be grown in culture by inoculation of Sabaraud's media. Caution is needed in the selection of culture media to exclude those that have cyclohexamide as this inhibits the growth of *Saprolegnia* [8]

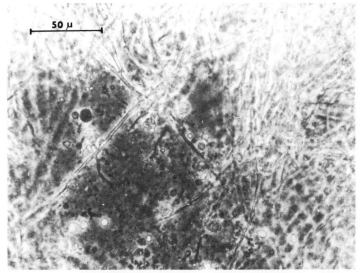

Fig. 9. Mycelium of *Saprolegnia*. Wet mount of scraping from mouth of Maroon Clown in Plate 12. Note branching of the hyphae.

INTERNAL FUNGI

The most important internal fungus infections in marine fish are caused by members of the class *Phycomycetes*, of which the best known is *Ichthyophonus (Ichthyosporidium hoferi)*.[25] The author has found this or a closely related fungus to be present in most exotic marine fish autopsied, with specimens from the Caribbean, Atlantic, Pacific, Indian oceans and China Sea represented. Because there remains considerable uncertainty with regard to the exact classification, it will be referred to as Ichthyophonus infection. The various stages of the life cycle

8. Greer, D. L. in Manual of Clinical Microbiology. Ed. Blair, J. E., Lennette, E. H., and Truant, J. P., Pub. Amer. Soc. for Microbiology, 1970, p 381.

25. Sindermann, C J. and Scattergood, L. W.: Diseases of Fishes of the Western North Atlantic. II. Ichthyosporidium Disease of the Sea Herring (Clupea harengus). Maine Dept. Sea Shore Fish, Res. Bull. No. 19, 1954. pp 1-40.

have not been completely elucidated, and there appears to be great variation in the prevalent form depending upon water temperature, and possibly pH and salinity. The forms of phycomycete fungi recognized in marine aquaria at temperatures of 70 to 82 degrees F. (21.1-26.7°C) are:

1. Zoospores — 2 - 4 μ flagellated bodies that are motile and are seen only in wet preparations of gills or of the body surface. Their shape, type and number of flagella, and method of movement are critical to the taxonomic classification of the fungus. Zoospores have not been described in Ichthyophonus.

2. Endoconidia[16] measuring 1.5 - 4 μ, are found in small clumps or large masses, and are heavily pigmented tan, brown or black. (Plate 33 & 34).

   These may be found in any organ of the body, but are most frequently seen in the spleen. The masses of encoconidia are often encysted by concentric layers of fibrous connective tissue cells that become partially hyalinized (Plate 35) producing, granulomas that have been confused with tuberculosis. (Plate 22).

3. Spores — Thick or thin walled spherical bodies about 4-6μ that may show germination with protrusion of a short blunt hypha. (Plate 36 & 37). The organism may be dark to golden brown in color.

4. Hyphae — These are rarely seen in fish at high temperatures ranging from 70 to 82°F (21.1-26.7°C). When they occur they are either of two types: macrohyphae measuring 7-15 μ in width and only slightly longer than wide, (Plate 38), and microhyphae that are approximately 2 μ in thickness, transparent, short, and tapered or tenuous; and all are non-septate.

5. *Sporangia* — fruiting bodies that measure 10-20 μ may be round, irregular or flask-shaped, and may have a short thin stalk. (Plate 40, 41, 42, 43 & Fig. 10).

6. Plasmodia — multinucleated cells capable of germination that are said to measure 18 to 150μ.

   Ichthyophonus is literally a time bomb within most fish, remaining quiescent while the fish is not greatly stressed. This fungus will proliferate in many organs and eventually kill the fish

16. Reichenbach-klinke, H. and Elkan, E.: Diseases of Fishes. Pub. Academic Press (London), 1965, p. 130.

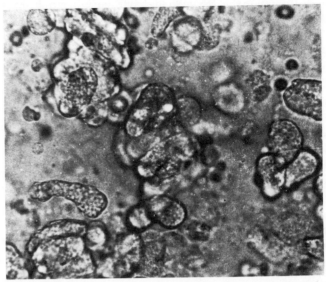

Fig. 10. Sporangia of a phycomycete fungus in wet mount of gill of *Coris gaimard*.

when environmental conditions are suboptimal and nutrition is poor (as in the aquarium). The organ most frequently infected is the spleen, but this may be almost completely destroyed without producing any overt signs of disease in the fish. Next in order of frequency is infection of the liver, kidneys, and brain. When the brain is affected, the most characteristic signs of this disease are seen — loss of balance (vertigo), listlessness, and exophthalmos. The gills are frequently infected, resulting in rapid breathing.

Demonstration of the Organism:

Equipment:

1. Microscope with achromatic lenses capable of 300 X magnification.
2. Glass microscope slides and coverslips.
3. Metal spatula or scraper.

Method:

Wet slide preparations are made from scrapings of the gills. The scrapings are coverslipped and examined with the microscope first at 100 X and then at 250 - 300 X. A supra-vital stain, brilliant cresyl blue, may be used to demonstrate the organisms. One drop of a 1:10,000 dilution should be added to the edge of the coverslip. Nuclei and cytoplasmic inclusions will stain dark blue. Another and better method is to examine stained histologic sections of the fish after autopsy. Paraffin block sections are required.

What to look for:

The sporangia (Plate 40, 41, 42, 43 & Fig. 10) will be visible as irregularly contoured elongated cells that usually taper toward one end. They may form aggregates in which the component cells are of different sizes and have flattened opposing sides and distinct cell walls. Spores may also be observed that are round or asymetric and show germination (Plates 36 & 37). The extreme variation in form and lack of any motility suggests that the cells under observation are fungal rather than protozoan.

LYMPHOCYSTIS

This disease is caused by a virus, the first described in fish. The virus produces numerous intracellular inclusion bodies, seen microscopically, and the cell reacts by giant hypertrophy (swelling). The infection usually occurs on a fin producing discrete small tumor-like growths variously described as cauliflower or raspberry-like. They are gray with smooth, rounded surfaces and appear to be tacked on.

The lymphocystis virus has been demonstrated by electron microscopy[17] [18], by ultra-filtration and virus transmission studies. The virus particles are about 200 mμ in size. The virus infects fibroblasts beneath the epithelium which in turn hypertrophy and may reach 500 μ in size (Plate 44 & 45). An inclusion body called the reticular body enlarges within the cell cytoplasm and the cell acquires a greatly thickened limiting membrane that is hyaline and may reach 10 μ in thickness. Approximately 9 months are required for the full size development of the lesion. The hypertrophied cells then degenerate and presumably virus particles are released.

Demonstration of the organism:

Equipment:

1. Microscope capable of 50 X magnification.

17. Walker, R.: The Structure of Lymphocyctis Virus of Fish. Virol. 18, 1962, pp. 503-505.
18. Walker, R. and Weissenberg, R.: Conformity of Light and Electron Microscopic Studies on Virus Particle Distribution in Lymphocystis Tumor Cells of Fish. Ann. N.Y. Acad. Sci., 126. 1965.

2. Glass microscope slides and coverslips.

3. Metal scraper, razor blade.

Method:

The infected fish is caught, hand held, and the lesion is scraped onto a glass slide. It is squashed or minced with a razor and a coverslip is added. It is pressed firmly down to get as thin a preparation as possible; the slide is then examined microscopically.

What to look for:

Clusters of very large cells with thick hyaline capsule-like walls will be seen with flattening of opposing sides.

GILL PARASITES

Gill flukes: These are "worms" belonging to the class *Trematoda*. There are three subclasses: *Aspidogastrea*, *Digenea*, and *Monogenea*. Gill flukes belong to the subclass *Monogenea* and differ from the other flukes that generally inhabit the internal organs by their method of reproduction which is very important with regard to treatment. While the digenetic trematodes have a complicated life cycle requiring one or more intermediate hosts other than fish, and therefore cannot spread in the aquarium, monogenetic trematodes have a simple life cycle that enables them to spread in the tank. Specific treatment is therefore necessary for any gill flukes in marine fish.

Wild fish frequently have gill flukes and their presence can be suspected when the fish shows rapid deep breathing with spreading and scratching of the opercula (gill covers). The fish may be removed and inspected by lifting the operculum with a toothpick and inspecting the gills for black spots resembling dirt[19], (Plate 46).

If they are seen the presumptive diagnosis is gill flukes. If they are not seen, the fish still may have gill flukes, especially with the above symptoms. Because the entire life cycle from adult to ova and from immature forms to adult, can occur very easily in the aquarium, since a host is readily available, it is necessary to treat the fish as soon as symptoms are seen.

Microscopic identification of the species of monogenetic trematode is very difficult and there are numerous species. The

9. Goldstein, R. J.: Monogenea. The Marine Aquarist 3, No. 5, 1972, pp 50-54.

Monogenea[20] have sucking discs with chitinous reinforcements. One of the most important families that parasitize the gills are the *Dactylogyridae*, characterized by four black eye spots at the anterior end. These organisms rarely exceed 1 mm in length. The family *Microcotylidae* has a number of genera that infect the gills of marine fish and are differentiated on the basis of the number (30 to 80) of suctorial discs. Two other families have representatives that infect gills: *Mazocraeidae* and *Diclidophoridae*.

Trichodina: Protozoan parasites belonging to the genus *Trichodina* number about eight species in marine fishes [21], [22], most of which infest the gills. They are small, flat, disc-like or hat-shaped organisms with circular rows of cilia and hooklets. The rim has fine long cilia while heavier cilia or teeth are arranged centrally. (Plate 47).   They attach by the outer ring of cilia and can erode the gill filament epithelium leaving bare segments of filaments. Red blood cells have been observed within them. While a heavy infestation itself may be fatal to the fish, a light infestation leaves the gills vulnerable to secondary bacterial infection[23].

Demonstration of the Organism:
Equipment:
1. Microscope with achromatic lenses and capable of at least 150 X.
2. Glass microscope slides and coverslips.
3. Metal spatula and teasing needles.

Method:
Prepare a wet mount of the gills of a fish that has recently died by removing several gill filaments and placing them on a slide. Strip away the lamellae from the cartilagenous ray so that a flat thin preparation is made. Add a drop of tank water and coverslip. It is now ready for microscopic examination.

20. Reichenbach-klinke, H. and Elkan, E.: The Principal Diseases of Lower Vertebrates, Diseases of Fishes. Acad. Press (London), 1965.
21. Tripathi, Y. R.: A New Species of Ciliate Trichodina branchicola from Some Fishes at Plymouth. J. Mar. Biol. Assn. U.K. 27, 1948. pp. 440-450.
22. Laird, M.: The Protozoa of New Zealand Intertidal Zone Fishes. Trans. Royal Soc. New Zealand. 81, 1953, pp. 79 - 143.
23. Padnos, M. and Nigrelli, R. F.: Trichodina spheroidesi and Trichodina halli spp Nov. Parasitic on the Gills and Skin of Marine Fishes, with Special Reference to the Life History of T. spheroidesi. Zoologica 27, 1942. pp 65 - 72.

What to look for:

Gill flukes will appear as large elongated structures that move spasmodically and have an assortment of internal organs (Plate 46). A dense cuticular wall surrounds the fluke.

The organisms of *Trichodina* measure about 50 μ in size and display a beautifully geometric arrangement of cilia in concentric rings (Plate 47). The cell is discoid with a peripheral ring of cilia.

INTESTINAL TREMATODES

Most flukes that infest the intestinal tract of marine fishes belong to the subclass *Digenea* of the class *Trematoda*. The digenetic trematodes have a complicated life cycle that involves intermediate hosts such as snails or possibly other invertebrates so that there is no danger of these parasites multiplying in the aquarium unless the snail or other invertebrate host happens to be present in the tank. In this case heavy infestations could result since thousands of larvae may be released from a single snail[24].

Wild fish are so frequently infested with intestinal trematodes that it is unusual to find one at autopsy that does not have at least several. A mild infection apparently causes no symptoms and is of no practical concern. The problem arises when the fish has a particularly heavy infestation, which can be lethal. There are several ways in which trematodes may cause severe injury; they may break through the gut wall with the concomitant release of bacteria causing peritonitis, or they may invade a major blood vessel such as the portal vein with obstruction of blood circulation, or they may enter the bile ducts causing obstruction and finally, they may be present in such numbers as to obstruct the intestine. Fish that are heavily infested frequently do not eat well, show signs of malnutrition such as poor coloration, and may develop a pinched or sunken appearance of the abdomen.

Demonstration of the Organism:

Trematodes anchor to the intestinal wall and are not shed in the feces, therefore it is necessary to autopsy the fish. The intestinal contents can be scraped onto a slide, coverslipped, and examined with any simple microscope. In such a wet preparation, the trematodes will be recognized by their large size,

24. Goldstein, R. J.: Digenea. The Marine Aquarist, 4, No. 2, 1973, pp 51-56.

suctorial disc or discs, and spasmodic contractions. Taxonomic classification is complex and beyond the purpose of this manual. It is based primarily upon the number and character of the organs of attachment. (Plate 48).

Plate 1. French Angel (*Pomacanthus paru*) with powdery white *Oodinium* infection over the entire body and fins.

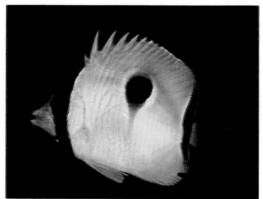

Plate 2. Teardrop Butterfly (*Chaetodon unimaculatus*) from Tahiti. Trophonts of *Cryptocaryon* ("White Spot Disease") are seen as pinhead size or period size (.) spots.

Plate 3. *Cryptocaryon* trophonts on fins of Sargeant Major (*Abudefuf saxitilis*) from Florida.

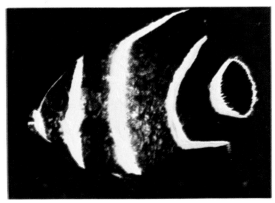

Plate 4. French Angel (*Pomacanthus paru*) from Jamaica. Advanced case of *Cryptocaryon* with trophonts on all fins, body, and eyes. The pigmented skin is denuded over the sides and susceptible to secondary bacterial infection.

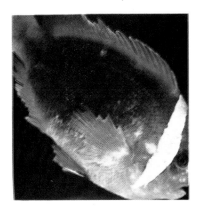

Plate 5. Tomato Clown (*Amphiprion frenatus*) with tuberculosis due to *Mycobacterium marinum*. Note the ragged reduction of fins, raised scales, and moth-eaten appearance that are characteristic of this disease.

Plate 6. Tomato Clown (*Amphiprion frenatus*) with tuberculosis due to *Mycobacterium marinum*. Note the protrusion of eye (exophthalmos), pale coloration with blotchy appearance and ragged fins. Very rapid breathing is also characteristic.

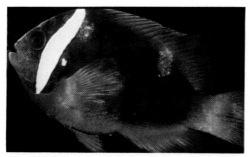

Plate 7. Tomato Clown (*Amphiprion frenatus*) with gray and milky white blotches on body and fins. Bacterial infection, probably *Pseudomonas* - *Aeromonas*.

Plate 8. Beau Gregory (*Pomacentrus leucostictus*). Fin, tail and body rot. Note skin hemorrhage in caudal peduncle.

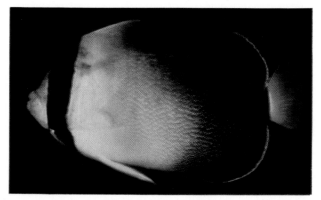

Plate 9. Singapore Angel (*Chaetodonopus mesoleucus*). Bacterial infection of lateral line and skin of head, probably caused by *Vibrio* sp.

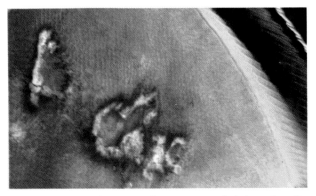

Plate 10. Enlarging ulcer secondary to traumatic injury. *Acanthurus glaucopareius*.

Plate 11. Healed ulcers six weeks after antibiotic treatment.

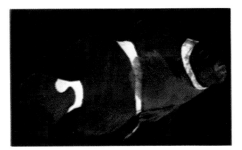

Plate 12. *Saprolegnia* sp. on the mouth of Maroon Clown (*Amphiprion biaculeatus*). Note the gray cottony appearance of the elevated lesion on the lower jaw.

Plate 13. *Lymphocystis* of mouth and tail of Royal Gramma (*Gramma loreto*). Note the papillomatous white growth composed of hypertrophied virus infected-cells of the host.

Plate 14. Exophthalmos (popeye) in Queen Angel (*Holacanthus ciliaris*).This fish was also blind. The optic tracts and brain as well as other organs were infected with *Ichthyophonus* disease (*Ichthyosporidium hoferi*). Note the open fixed mouth characteristic of this disease.

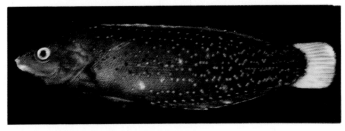

Plate 15. *Coris gaimard* with dark nodules beneath the skin due to Ichthyophonus (*Ichthyosporidium hoferi*).

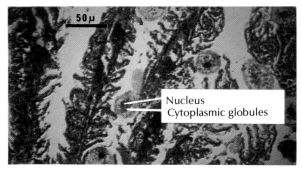

Plate 16. Gill of Parrotfish with 8 distinct vegetative cells of *Oodinium ocellatum*. Note the distinct nucleus and cytoplasmic globules. Paraffin section, H&E stain.

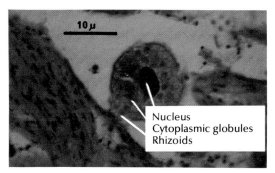

Plate 17. Attached vegetative stage of *O. ocellatum* in gill of Blue Head Wrasse. Note the point of attachment where the rhizoids penetrate the gill filament stroma. Paraffin section, H&E stain.

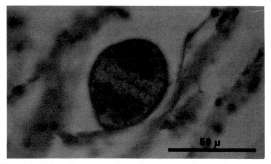

Plate 18. Palmella stage of *Oodinium ocellatum* from gill of Parrotfish. Note division into two cells in progress. Paraffin section, H&E stain.

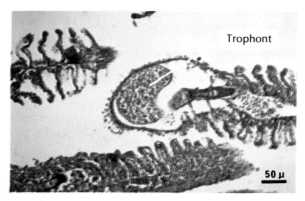

Plate 19. Trophont of *Cryptocaryon* within gill filament of Coral Beauty Angel. H&E stain, paraffin block section. The organism distends and partially occludes the blood vessel.

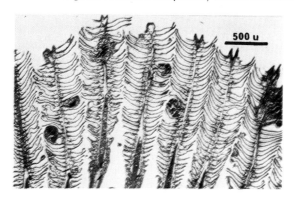

Plate 20. Tuberculosis (*Mycobacterium marinum*) producing granulomas in gill filaments. At least 7 such lesions are seen. Paraffin section, H&E stain from Tomato Clown (*Amphiprion frenatus*).

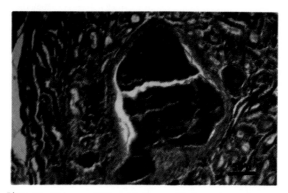

Plate 21. Kidney of Gray Mojarra with large irregular centrally necrotic granuloma. Note the peripheral laminar fibrous encapsulation. Paraffin section, H&E stain.

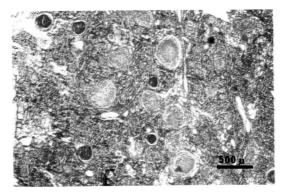

Plate 22. Kidney of Tomato Clown with numerous large pale tuberculous granulomas (*Mycobacterium marinum*). The smaller dark granulomas are caused by *Ichthyophonus*. Paraffin section, H&E stain.

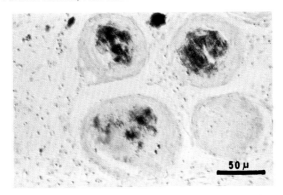

Plate 23. Acid fast stain showing *Mycobacterium marinum* bacilli in granulomas of retrobulbar region in Tomato Clown. Paraffin section, Ziehl-Neelsen stain.

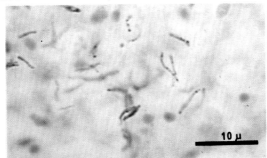

Plate 24. *Mycobacterium marinum*, acid fast stain. From splenic granuloma in Yellow-Tail Blue Devil. Note the beaded appearance of the slender red rods.

Plate 25. Tuberculosis (*Mycobacterium marinum*) cultural growth on Middlebrook 7H10 media. The colonies are characteristically lemon yellow, elevated, smooth and moist. Growth is first noted in two weeks. Sebae Clown.

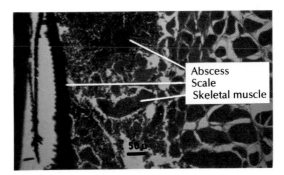

Plate 26. Skin and skeletal muscle with lateral line abscess. Singapore Angel (*Chaetodonopus mesoleucus*). Paraffin section, H&E stain.

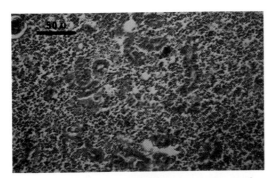

Plate 27. Acute nephritis in Blue Tang (*Paracanthurus hepatus*). There is extensive necrosis of kidney with scattered tubules remaining, and acute inflammation. Paraffin section, H&E stain.

77

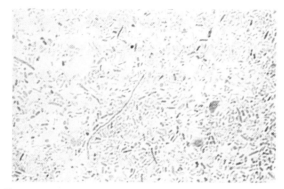

Plate 28. Gram negative bacilli, mixed growth from culture plate.

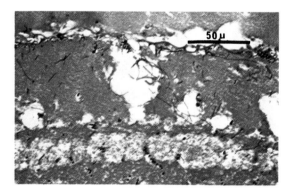

Plate 29. *Columnaris* disease due to *Chondrococcus colum-naris* in brain of Rock Beauty Angel. Paraffin section, H&E stain.

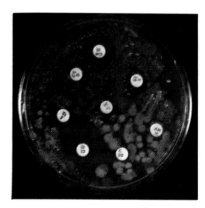

Plate 30. Antibiotic sensitivity discs on plate (Petri dish). Mixed bacterial culture. All organisms are sensitive only to colistin sulfate (CL).

78

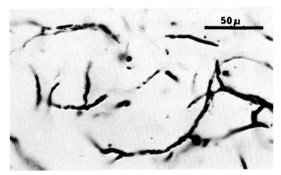

Plate 31. *Saprolegnia* from Maroon Clown, Plate 12. Paraffin section, Gram's stain. Note that the hyphae are Gram positive and branching.

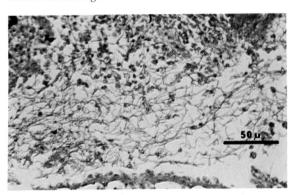

Plate 32. Mycelium of *Saprolegnia* infiltrating and destroying tissue. From mouth of Maroon Clown shown in Plate 12. Paraffin section, H&E stain.

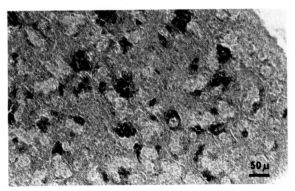

Plate 33. Spleen of Three-Striped Butterfly. Note large aggregates of brown pigmented endoconidia of *Ichthyophonus*. Paraffin block section, H&E stain.

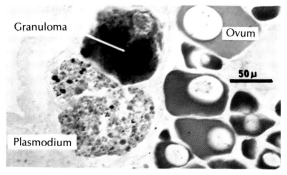

Plate 34. Granuloma and probable plasmodium of *Ichthyophonus* in capsule of ovary of Tomato Clown. Paraffin block section, Giemsa stain.

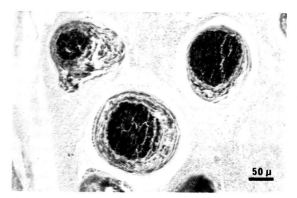

Plate 35. *Ichthyophonus* granulomas in spleen of Tomato Clown. Paraffin block section, Giemsa stain. Note thick fibrous lamination of cyst walls.

Plate 36. Germinating spore of the phycomycete fungus of *Ichthyophonus* in peritoneum of a High Hat. Note brown pigmentation and heavy capsule.

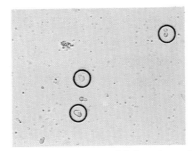

Plate 37. Phycomycete (*Ichthyophonus*) in gill. Wet mount of Blue Devil. Germinating spores.

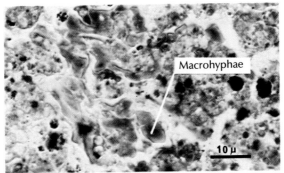

Macrohyphae

10 μ

Plate 38. Macrohyphae and pigmented endoconidia of *Ichthyophonus* in liver of Ocellaris Clown. Paraffin block section, Masson's trichrome stain.

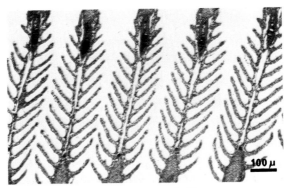

100 μ

Plate 39. Normal gill.

81

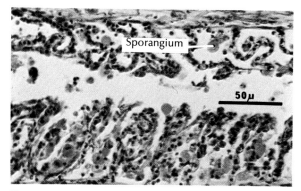

Plate 40. Gill of Clown Sweetlips heavily infected with phycomycete fungus. Note sporangia. Paraffin block section, H&E stain.

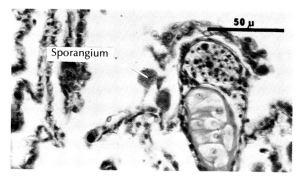

Plate 41. Gill of Ocellaris Clown with sporangia of phycomycete fungus. Paraffin block section, Masson's trichrome stain.

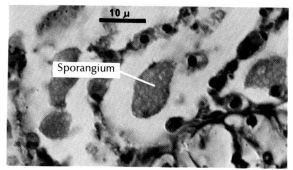

Plate 42. Gill of Sebae Clown with sporangia of phycomycete fungus. Paraffin block section, H&E stain.

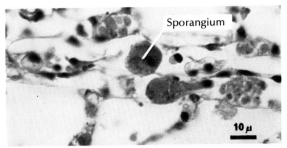

Plate 43. Gill of Ocellaris Clown with sporangia of phycomycete fungus. Paraffin block section, H&E stain.

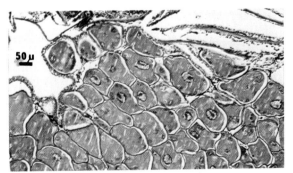

Plate 44. Lymphocystis from fin of Fox-Faced Rabbitfish. Fibroblasts containing abundant viral DNA show great hypertrophy. Paraffin section, H&E stain.

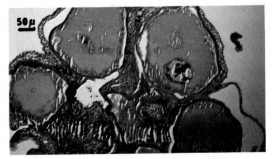

Plate 45. Lymphocystis from Royal Gramma in Plate 13. Note the greatly thickened hyaline walls and cytoplasmic inclusions.

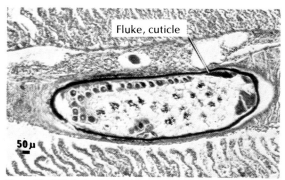

Plate 46. Gill fluke lodged between filaments from Regal Angel. A thick dense cuticle surrounds the body and the central organoid structure is visible. Paraffin section, H&E stain.

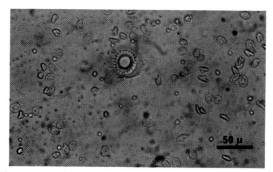

Plate 47. *Trichodina* in wet mount of gill from Ocellaris Clown. Note the geometric arrangement of specialized cilia.

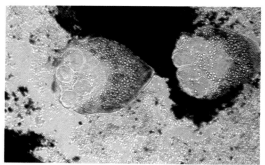

Plate 48. Digenetic trematodes from intestine of Gray Mojarra in wet mount. Many suctorial discs are seen, the number varies in different species. Phase contrast microscopy.

I. Temperature

Degrees Fahrenheit (°F)	Degrees Centigrade (°C)
60	15.6
61	16.1
62	16.7
63	17.2
64	17.8
65	18.3
66	18.9
67	19.4
68	20
69	20.6
70	21.1
71	21.7
72	22.2
73	22.8
74	23.3
75	23.9
76	24.4
77	25
78	25.6
79	26.1
80	26.7
81	27.2
82	27.8
83	28.3
84	28.9
85	29.4
86	30
87	30.6
88	31.1
89	31.7
90	32.2
91	32.8
92	33.3
93	33.9
94	34.4
95	35

II. Liquid Measure

	Abbreviation
1 Milliliter - 1 Cubic centimeter	1 ml - 1 cc
1 Teaspoon - about 5 milliliters or cubic centimeters	1 tsp - 5 ml - 5 cc
1 Tablespoon - about 15 milliliters	1 tbs - 15 ml
1 Ounce - 29.6 milliliters	1 oz - 29.6 ml
1 Pint - 473 milliliters	1 pt - 473 ml
1 Pint - 16 ounces	1 pt - 16 oz
1 Pint - .473 liters	1 pt - .473 L
1 Liter - 1,000 milliliters	1 L - 1,000 ml
1 Quart - 32 ounces	1 qt - 32 oz
1 Quart - 2 pints	1 qt - 2 pt
1 Quart - .95 liters	1 qt. - .95 L
1 Gallon - 4 quarts	1 gal - 4qt
1 Gallon - 3.8 liters	1 gal - 3.8 L

III. Weights

1 Grain - .065 grams	1 gr - .065 g
1 Gram - 1000 milligrams	1 g - 1000 mg
1 Milligram - 1000 micrograms	1 mg - 1000 μg
1 Gram - 15.4 grains	1 g - 15.4 gr
1 Ounce - 28.4 grams	1 oz - 28.4 g
1 Kilogram - 1000 grams	1 k - 1000 g
1 Kilogram - 2.2 pounds	1 k - 2.2 lb
1 Pound - .45 kilograms	1 lb - .45 k

IV. Length

1 Millimeter - 1000 micrometers (microns)	1 mm - 1000 μ
1 Centimeter - 10 millimeters	1 cm - 10 mm
1 Centimeter - .39 inches	1 cm - .39 in
	.39''
1 Inch - 2.54 centimeters	1 in - 2.54 cm
1 Foot - .3 meters	1 ft - .3 m
1 Meter - 3.28 feet	1 m - 3.28 ft
1 Yard - 3 feet	1 yd - 3 ft
1 Yard - .91 meters	1 yd - .91 m

V. Capacity

1 Gallon - 231 cubic inches	1 gal - 231 cu in or in^3

Tank capacity - length X width X height in inches divided by 231, in gallons.

VI. Abbreviations

% - per cent or parts per hundred

‰ - parts per thousand

ppm - parts per million

mg % - milligrams per 100 milligrams. Usually used as milligrams of a chemical per 100 milliliters of water (since 1 milliliter of water weighs 1 milligram)

VII. Other useful measures

1 Cubic foot of seawater weighs 64 pounds

1 Cubic foot of fresh water weighs 62.4 pounds

Fresh water has a density or specific gravity of 1 (sp g = 1)

Saltwater is more dense and the specific gravity is about 1.023

pH - hydrogen ion concentration. A measure of acidity or alkalinity. It is expressed as the logarithm of the reciprocal of the hydrogen ion concentration. Therefore if a solution has 10^{-7} hydrogen ions per liter, the acidity is expressed as pH 7. The scale ranges from 0 to 14. Between 0 - 7 is the acid range and between 7 - 14 is the alkaline rante. 7 is neutral.

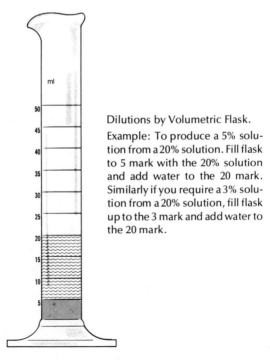

Dilutions by Volumetric Flask.

Example: To produce a 5% solution from a 20% solution. Fill flask to 5 mark with the 20% solution and add water to the 20 mark. Similarly if you require a 3% solution from a 20% solution, fill flask up to the 3 mark and add water to the 20 mark.

GLOSSARY

Aerobic	Requiring oxygen for life.
Antibiotic	A substance produced by a micro-organism having the capacity to inhibit the growth or kill another micro-organism.
Cytoplasm	The fluid protoplasm of a cell, as distinguished from the nucleus.
Diatom	Unicellular algae with silica cell walls abundant in plankton.
Dinoflagellate	One celled organisms having two flagella, one terminal and the other encircling the cell in a groove.
Dinospore	The newly hatched free swimming stage of a dinoflagellate.
DNA	Deoxyribonucleic Acid. One of the principal constituents of genes found within the nucleus.
Epithelium	The cellular tissue layer that covers the surface or lines tubes or cavities of an animal.
Granuloma	A tissue nodule composed of chronic inflammatory cells.
Host	A living animal or plant providing subsistance or lodgement to a parasite.
Hypertrophy	Excessive increase in size of a cell or organ.
Hypha	One of the individual filaments that make up the mycelium of a fungus.
Interferon	An antiviral protein formed by cells in response to a viral infection.
Ionize	To convert to an ion a particle carrying an electrical charge. The result of an atom gaining or losing one or more electrons.
Lysozyme	A protein present in biological secretions that is capable of attacking the capsules of various bacteria.
Metazoa	Animals having a multi-celled body in which the cells are differentiated into tissue; as opposed to protozoa.
Mycelium	The mass of interwoven hyphae forming the vegetative portion of a fungus.
Necrosis	Tissue or cell death.
Osmotic	Capable of osmosis; the diffusion of water through a membrane in such a way that a more

	concentrated solution on one side of the membrane is diluted.
Pathogen	An agent capable of causing disease.
pH	Hydrogen ion concentration, described fully under Table VII, page 87.
Proteolytic	A substance capable of breaking down proteins.
Protozoa	Single celled animal.
Rhizoid	The thread-like filament of a cell used for nutrition and anchoring.
Scoliosis	Lateral curvature of the spine.
Tomite	The earliest free swimming stage of certain ciliate protozoa.
Trematode	A parasitic flatworm.
Ubiquitous	Occurring or capable of appearing everywhere.

INDEX

Bold numbers indicate numbers of plates in color plate section.